CAUSE AND EFFECT

CAUSE
AND EFFECT

The Hayden Colloquium on Scientific Method and Concept

EDITED BY

DANIEL LERNER

CONTRIBUTORS

Robert A. Dahl Ernst Mayr
Lewis S. Feuer Ernest Nagel
Abraham Kaplan Talcott Parsons
Daniel Lerner Paul A. Samuelson
Herbert A. Simon

THE FREE PRESS, New York
COLLIER-MACMILLAN LIMITED, London

For
Louise, Tom, Amy
Causes and Effects

PREFACE

THE HAYDEN COLLOQUIUM of the Massachusetts Institute of Technology is a distinguished lecture series concerned with common problems of concept and method in the diverse fields of modern knowledge. Each year the Colloquium selects a classic theme that has preoccupied thinkers over many generations, sometimes over centuries. The lecturers are asked to clarify the meaning of this classic theme for contemporary work in their own field of knowledge. How are the problems historically associated with this theme encountered by living people concerned with theory, research, and judgment in fields ranging from aesthetics to zoology? How have new versions of the old problems been set and met? To what extent is the traditional formulation of these problems no longer relevant to contemporary needs? In those cases where the contemporary formulation is more appropriate to current thinking, but is so stated as to leave the older problem unsolved, what importance has the unsolved residue?

To questions such as these our lecturers respond in terms of work-in-progress, and their responses are critically discussed by the members of the Colloquium. This procedure has produced over the years a continuing conversation among the various fields of knowledge. Common problems of considerable breadth and depth have emerged. It has appeared worthwhile to preserve these lectures in book form. The first three sessions of the Colloquium were published by The Free Press as *Evidence and Inference, Quantity and Quality, Parts and Wholes.*

The present volume, *Cause and Effect,* completes the quartet as planned and concludes the Hayden Colloquium for the present. The papers in this volume are based mainly on lectures delivered to the Hayden Colloquium during the academic year 1960-1961. In a few cases, the discussion that followed the lecture was sufficiently interesting (and its tape-recording sufficiently clear) to warrant inclusion. These convey some sense of the intellectual style of the meetings, and in several places sharpen the philosophical or scientific issues arising from the lectures. The paper by Abraham Kaplan was presented to a joint meeting of the Colloquium and the Plurel, association of M.I.T. graduate students in political science, early in 1964. The papers by Herbert A. Simon and Lewis S. Feuer are here reprinted by the kind permission, respectively, of John Wiley and *The Journal of Philosophy*.

The Hayden Colloquium was designed to explore classic problems of scientific concept and method as they recur in the contemporary research framework. Accordingly, our focus has been on the operational meaning of evidence, quantification, part-whole relations, and causality for men engaged in the daily work of science. We have not slighted the counsel of philosophers of science —here represented by Ernest Nagel and Abraham Kaplan—but we have given priority to interpretations of their own experience by men who have had to shape these concepts into working tools of their own special trades. Nor have we slighted the humanities and learned professions, since papers were presented to the successive Colloquia on the problems of architecture, engineering, history, law, medicine, poetry, and psychoanalysis, but we have given priority to current work in the natural and social sciences.

In retrospect, these four volumes present a panorama of the classic issues of concept and method in the perspective of contemporary science. They reveal wide furrows of common seed, and strong growths of common fruit, in science. It is to be hoped that the colloquy sustained at M.I.T. over the past seven years, and represented in these four volumes, will stimulate continuing conversation elsewhere among men responsible for the advancement, application, and diffusion of knowledge in our contemporary world—a world that is coming to recognize knowledge as the most priceless of human assets.

The making of such books represents the cooperative work of many hands. The lecture series has been sponsored by the M.I.T. School of Humanities and Social Studies, from funds granted by the Carnegie Corporation of New York. Dean John E. Burchard made the Colloquium possible and has been its firm supporter throughout. Professor Max F. Millikan chaired the *Cause and Effect* sessions of the Colloquium during my sabbatical leave. Dr. Morton Gorden solved the difficult problems of recording hot discussions on cool tapes. Miss Judith Weinstein and Mrs. Pauline Jacintho labored mightily to produce typescripts from taped sounds. Richard W. Hatch put his great editorial skills to work on preparing the manuscript for publication. My wife, Jean Lerner, as usual carried the ball to the goal. To all these people, as to the participants in the Hayden Colloquium who made all this effort worthwhile, I am deeply grateful.

DANIEL LERNER

CONTENTS

PREFACE   vii

INTRODUCTION, ON CAUSE AND EFFECT   1
    Daniel Lerner

TYPES OF CAUSAL EXPLANATION IN SCIENCE   11
    Ernest Nagel
  DISCUSSION

CAUSE AND EFFECT IN BIOLOGY   33
    Ernst Mayr

CAUSE AND EFFECT IN SOCIOLOGY   51
    Talcott Parsons
  DISCUSSION

CAUSE AND EFFECT IN THE STUDY OF POLITICS   75
    Robert A. Dahl
  DISCUSSION

SOME NOTIONS ON CAUSALITY AND TELEOLOGY IN ECONOMICS 99
    Paul A. Samuelson

NONCAUSAL EXPLANATION   145
    Abraham Kaplan

CAUSAL ORDERING AND IDENTIFIABILITY   157
    Herbert A. Simon

CAUSALITY IN THE SOCIAL SCIENCES   191
    Lewis S. Feuer

On Cause and Effect

Daniel Lerner

"Cause me no causes!" exclaimed the Elizabethan dramatist Massinger. After the punning fashion of his time, he wittily expressed one ambiguity underlying the philosophical analysis of causation that plagued his forbears and recurs among his posterity.[1] The pun conjoins cause as effort with cause as effect. Rendered literally —and thereby deprived of its literary interest—the injunction might read: "Produce no effect upon me that will oblige me to make efforts!"

Since the earliest records of human thought—though thinking about causation surely antedates our records—philosophical men have sought to differentiate the personal cause by which one is *motivated to act* from the transpersonal cause by which events are *made to occur*. The depersonalization of causality was an important step toward clarity—and the step was a long time coming.

A full generation before Christ, Publius Syrus had written in his *Maxims:* "No one should be judge in his own cause" (Maxim 545). Centuries later, the Catholic philosopher Pascal reaffirmed this ancient wisdom for modern times: "It is not permitted to the most equitable of men to be a judge in his own cause" (*Pensées,* Ch. IV, 1). The modern Jewish philosopher Spinoza supplied a psychological explanation why causation should be depersonalized: "Self-complacency is pleasure accompanied by the idea of oneself as cause" (*Ethics,* Proposition 51, note). It was into Caesar's mouth, after all, that Shakespeare put the fallacy of oneself-as-cause; and the irony was clear when the tyrant's tragic end was foreshadowed by his assertion: "The cause is in my will: I will not come" (*Julius Caesar,* Act II, Scene 2).

[1] An illuminating explication of the philosophical resonances in poetic ambiguities is William Empson, *Seven Types of Ambiguity* (1953).

But the depersonalization of causality did not diminish its interest for thinking men. If the idea that causes are not coterminous with personal motives is one major theme of our intellectual history, its corollary is that causes exist and are discernible in the effects they produce. The same Shakespeare who located Caesar's downfall in his faulty view of oneself-as-cause elsewhere exclaimed: "There is occasions and causes, why and wherefore in all things" (*Henry IV*, Act V, Scene 1). Or, more briefly: "Every why hath a wherefore" (*Comedy of Errors*, Act II, Scene 2). The same Spinoza who relegated oneself-as-cause to the vanities did so only within the context of his more general prior assertion: "Nothing exists from whose nature some effect does not follow" (*Ethics*, Proposition 36).

The conviction that a rational universe requires a concept of causation was ingrained as well in the philosophical thinking of Americans. In his treatise on *The Freedom of the Will* (1754), one of the shaping documents of the American philosophical tradition, Jonathan Edwards plainly proclaimed: "I assert that nothing ever comes to pass without a cause." The testimony of the American Puritan provides a valuable philosophical link with the suspect French Jansenist and the excommunicated Dutch Marrano-Jew. The "advanced" thinking of Edwards, Pascal, Spinoza—which rendered them suspect to their more doctrinaire contemporaries —reveal in retrospect the indispensable bondage of Judaism, Catholicism, and Protestantism to a common concept of causation. Without it, a divinely ordered world became inexplicable to them and philosophy lost its vocation.

For we are dealing with those centuries—most of those fifty or more centuries since men began to explain their environment as an ordered universe—when every philosophy had, first, to come to terms with a theology. It is only in the past century, with the Darwinian theory of evolution, that there has emerged a rational theory which ordered the universe of living things without need for a deity or a theology. So powerfully did this theory move men's minds, so rapidly did it win their support, that a mere century later we can barely appreciate the depths of feeling that had been invested in the theological concept of causation over all the prior centuries of human history.

In the century before Darwin, when natural science was already moving steadily in the direction of secular theories witnessed only by empirical testimony, the poets published their protests. The Romantics based their case on the simple assertion of the natural order as prima facie evidence of the divine order, *vide* William Cowper: "Nature is but a name for an effect/Whose cause is God" (*The Winter Walk at Noon*). The sterner Rationalists made a more elaborate argument for the fading theological concept. Alexander Pope—who apostrophized "Thou First Great Cause, least understood!"—warned philosophy that its own death warrant was sealed in the coffin of theology. *The Dunciad,* his bitter satire of contemporary thinking, asserted:

> Philosophy, that lean'd on Heav'n before,
> Shrinks to her second cause, and is no more.

The passing of philosophical commitment to a Prime Mover raised more theoretical problems than it solved. When the infinite regression of a causal sequence could no longer be traced back to a "First Great Cause," then analytical ambiguities in the theory of causation were bound to appear. This problem had been plainly foreseen in the philosophical discourse of the ancient Greeks— before the monistic clarity of theological causation had prevailed in the West. Reviewing the ambiguity of pre-monist Greek philosophy, Diogenes Laertius wrote: "Anaximander used to assert that the primary cause of all things was the Infinite—not defining exactly whether he meant air or water or anything else."

Modern philosophy, in its post-monist quest to escape the dilemma of ambiguity, took a decisive turn in its theory that causation required neither a single nor a final cause. The turn was in the direction of pluralism: thenceforth causality was to be multidimensional and dynamic.

The major themes were sounded by the philosophic expositors of Darwinism. Herbert Spencer put the multidimensional proposition plainly in his key essay *On Progress:* "Every cause produces more than one effect." The formulation of dynamism was rather more complex, and rather less comprehensive, for it is no easy matter to build a causal concept around causes that are neither single nor even final. The newer concept of causation as multidimensional and temporal led philosophical men to embrace the idea of *process*. As Viscount Morley put the matter in his exposition of Darwinian theory: "Evolution is not a force but a process; not a cause but a law" (*On Compromise*).

This sentence encapsulated several issues which were to preoccupy scientists and philosophers in the next generations. But the issues were too complex for popular taste—lacking the forceful clarity of a "First Great Cause" (which often served also as Last and Only Cause). The literary intelligentsia, already sensitive and irritable about their widening distance from the powerful new sciences, found such philosophic concepts too obscure to accept —or even to understand. Some snarled; others snickered (e.g., Gilbert and Sullivan). The run-of-the-mill literati gave up the whole thing as a bad show:

> Events are writ by history's pen
>   Though causes are too much to care for;
> Fame talks about the where and when,
>   While folly asks the why and wherefore.[2]

This is a far cry from Shakespeare's confident "Every why hath a wherefore!" It represents fairly the impact of modern science via philosophy upon the orderly universe of traditional thought—a universe rendered so clear and comprehensible over the centuries, indeed, as to seem the universe of common sense itself. Small wonder that the new ideas of an evolutionary humanity in a relativist environment appeared to skew the common-sense universe so that "things are seldom what they seem." Small wonder too that this topsy-turvy new universe engendered, among people less blithe about the cosmos than W. S. Gilbert, a "crisis of confidence" that has persisted into our own day.

The new concept of causation was an agent, as well as a

[2] W. M. Praed, "Epitaph on the Late King of the Sandwich Islands."

symptom, of this malady. It does shake one's confidence to be told, by apparently authoritative spokesmen, that one doesn't really know why things happen as they do. It is even more unnerving to be told, on high authority, that some things happen that shouldn't. Whither, under these conditions, the calm confidence of John Dryden that "whatever is, is in its causes just" (*Oedipus,* Act III, Scene 1)? If it is not true that reality is produced by just (even if inscrutable) causes, then what are we to believe about causation —what, indeed, are we to believe about justice?

One strong modern tradition, descended from David Hume, takes the view that the less we believe about causation the better. Bertrand Russell expressed this view with characteristic pungency: "The Law of Causality, I believe, like much that passes among philosophers, is a relic of a bygone age, surviving like the monarchy, only because it is erroneously supposed to do no harm." Russell based this conclusion upon his understanding of modern science, which conducted its operations and achieved its results without any need for causal laws. On this ground Russell ungently chided all philosophical traditions past and present: "All philosophers, of every school, imagine that causation is one of the fundamental axioms of science, yet, oddly enough, in advanced science . . . the word 'cause' never occurs."

The papers collected in this volume deal in different ways with the questions raised by Russell. In the conduct of the contemporary sciences what need, if any, is there for causal concepts? Which concepts are especially useful in which sciences? Is there an underlying conception of causality that is common in all scientific work today? Can any formulation be made that is generally acceptable to contemporary scientists? Such queries as these, John P. Roche reminds us, invoke the Talmudic caveat that the existence of a question does not necessarily require the existence of an answer.

The difficulty of learning whether there exists "an answer" to these questions is further complicated in the present case by the tacit ideology of contemporary scientists, who exalt the practice of research while often deprecating the theory of research (methodology). It is customary for practicing scientists to claim a "trained incapacity," or, in more sophisticated style, a disciplined disinterest, in dealing with the logic of what they do. This conventional disclaimer of methodological insight or interest has been evident throughout the years of the Hayden Colloquim. Yet, the published record shows that many scientists turn out to be quite adept in handling the "philosophical" problems of their own disciplines and of science generally. Albert Ando has put the matter plainly:

To most of us who spend our professional lives in scientific inquiry, questions of epistemology and methodology tend to be as remote and distasteful as the most recent discoveries in biochemical research laboratories are to ordinary farmers. Many scientists make significant contributions to knowledge unhindered by, even aided by, their disinterest in formal problems of methodology. Yet, unlike farmers who can confidently depend on others to be concerned with the biochemistry of porcine metabolism, scientists must, when it becomes necessary, face the methodological and epistemological questions themselves.

From those who have faced the methodological problems themselves we learn, despite the reticence imposed upon scientists by their tacit ideology, that the makings of a new scientific consensus are at hand. We have no way of knowing what coefficient to assign to the present state of this consensus; nor are we prepared to defend the proposition that consensus among scientists is a simple frequency distribution of opinions. It is more likely that among scientists, as other men, a consensus is produced by a type of Brownian (or even Bandwagon) effect, wherein a few acknowledged leaders in scientific work set out an explicit codification of scientific methodology that is acceptable to the reticent many.

The Hayden Colloquium has shown that some elements of a scientific consensus do exist. Perhaps the most important of these is the widespread agreement that science now operates in a probabalistic universe. Herbert A. Simon tells us that "the viewpoint is becoming more and more prevalent that the appropriate scientific model of the world is not a deterministic model but a probabilistic one." This viewpoint is an operational code with consequences for physics as well as metaphysics, for mathematics as well as methodology. These consequences are exhibited by any scientific model that expresses the relationships between its variables, not in deterministic differential equations, but in probability coefficients. Where the calculus of probabilities replaces differential calculus, more than a convenient exchange of notational systems has occurred. Probabilistic notation is more "convenient" precisely because it better represents the hypotheses and the tests—the evidence and the inference—that figure in contemporary scientific work.

The probabilistic trend of contemporary science reformulates the concept of causality but does not obviate it. When we say, at the conclusion of a correlational analysis, that two or more variables "go together" in a certain numerical relationship, we choose to emphasize their concurrence without committing ourselves on their causality. Recent advances in multivariate analysis have doubtless been facilitated by this strategy of ignoring the question of causal relationship. Ignoring the question, however, need not entail begging the question.

The causal question can safely be ignored so long as there is no reason to doubt that the relationship between the variables in a model is symmetrical. When the relationship is symmetrical, the variables are "interdependent" in the sense that their joint occurrence is mutually caused or reciprocally determined. The rate of their joint occurrence (or nonoccurrence) in any situation hypothesized by the investigator then becomes the essential piece of information. For, so long as this rate is sufficiently high to validate predictions and controls based upon it, the investigator has no need to know anything more "philosophical" about the relationship.

However, when the rate of joint occurrence is low or erratic, additional information is needed to eliminate the observed errors and to obtain a more accurate model of the relationship. One line of inquiry is to test for a "spurious" relationship—to show that the connections between the variables, as hypothesized by the model, are not "necessary." Another is to test for a "causal" relationship—to show that the variables are connected, but not symmetrically, that the assumption of mutual and reciprocal "interdependence" is untenable.

To do this requires reordering of the variables in relation to each other and produces a different model. When two variables are functionally related (or "interdependent"), A is related to B in the same way that B is related to A. This does not hold when the two variables are causally related, since A can cause B without B being able to cause A. This is the asymmetrical shape of the causal relationship that Professor Simon uses to work out "a clear and rigorous basis for determining when a causal ordering can be said to hold between two variables or groups of variables in a model." We have included Simon's fine paper in this volume because it corrects some faulty current notions and shows why the term "cause," despite its "generally unsavory epistemological status," nevertheless "can perform a useful function and should be retained."

We have included the paper by Lewis S. Feuer, which, like Simon's, was not presented to the Hayden Colloquium. because it deals clearly and provocatively with another issue on which the tacit ideology of contemporary scientists sometimes appears to be misleading. This is the relationship between the personal values of scientists and the objective methods of science, a hardy perennial of academic debate that is as imbued with ambiguity as Massinger's "Cause me no causes!" In the contemporary setting of science, the issue has consumed volumes of printed discussions on the ethics of nuclear research.

The social sciences, with their postwar focus on such topics as race relations, arms control, economic development, and nation building, have also been subject to barrages of moral controversy over issues that might be better clarified by more temperate methodological analysis. It would surely help to know just how a scientist's personal values do, in fact, affect his work before delivering a judgment that this affect is a Bad Thing—or a Good Thing!

Professor Feuer's thesis on this cluster of issues is nicely formed and lucidly phrased. The baggage of personal values carried by the social scientist is labeled "his meta-sociological convictions." These are expressed in a choice between two broad modes of social analysis called "interventionist" and "necessitarian" models.

The former presumes "that men can intervene in social situations to change conditions and determine, in significant measure, the direction of trends;" the latter presumes the contrary. Feuer argues that "contemporary social science is increasingly giving adherence to an interventionist mode of thought."

Feuer's argument can be assimilated to the Simon thesis presented above—namely, that contemporary science increasingly works with probabilistic rather than deterministic models. A necessitarian mode of thought requires determinism; an interventionist mode is untenable under determinism but is readily compatible with probabilism. The interest of Feuer's argument, however, goes beyond its methodological propositions. It confronts contemporary social science with its own social environment, considered as a particular phase in the flow of historical events. If historical periods differ so markedly as we are told, he argues, "it may be the case that human decision counts for more in certain social systems than in others."

In those systems where "human decision counts for more" interventionist models are more likely to suit the values of scientists. Also (should we say "because?") they provide more valid prediction and control of events. It follows that in such systems the prevailing concepts of causality will be different from the concepts current in systems where human decisions count for less and necessitarian models are favored.

We have carried Feuer's argument beyond the point at which he left it—perhaps beyond the point at which he would accept it—because these reminders of the historicity of social systems, and of the different environments that social systems provide for scientific concepts and methods, are eminently appropriate to conclude a volume focused on the usage of causality in contemporary science. Our contemporary world is an astonishing place. It is a world that in one generation has produced greater transformations in some sectors of human activity than all of preceding history. Among the widest and deepest of these transformations is the scientific enterprise itself. We have the word of an eminent historian that most of history's scientists are living today—i.e., that our contemporary world contains more scientists than lived in all precious societies recorded in history.

This staggering fact must give us pause. We take for granted the pervasive activity of science and its allied technologies of construction and destruction. We also take for granted the morality tales told about science, which come roughly to the allegation that when it is good it is very, very good and when it is bad it is horrid. But we cannot take for granted the intellectual processes of contemporary science, for none but ourselves can grant this knowledge.

This volume seeks to understand the contemporary sense of causation—and thereby to connect our own activity with the great scientific tradition of past societies via a key intellectual issue for science in all times and places. Causation is not equally necessary to all scientific procedures and practices, but a theoretical understanding of how causation figures in its own activity *is* necessary to any self-critical and self-regulating science—a science that aims to predict and control its own activity with the same rationality that it applies to other activities in its social environment. That understanding is the aim of this book.

Types of Causal Explanation
in Science

ERNEST NAGEL

THE search for particular causal connections in nature is generally
acknowledged to be a task for empirical rather than philosophical
inquiry. This search is often successful, despite the fact that it is
commonly carried on by men who have reflected little, if at all,
on what they understand by the term "cause," or even on what the
requirements are for making warranted assertions about causal
connections. Lack of clarity about these matters can frequently
hinder the advance of knowledge, and clarification may therefore
be an important phase in the development of science. Such clarification has been traditionally regarded as a philosophical under-
taking, though practicing scientists as well as professional philosophers continue to pursue it.

Philosophical discussions of causality are, for the most part,
centered on two major questions. The first is the explication of the
notion of cause, with the aim of exhibiting its component ideas
and identifying the contexts of its significant application. The
second is the articulation of the methodology of causal inquiry, in
order to codify, assess, and (when necessary) correct accepted
canons for judging the validity of causal imputations. Although
these questions are related, the present paper deals almost exclusively with limited aspects of the first one.

I

Many influential scientists and philosophers have argued that
the notion of cause plays a diminishing role in modern science,
especially in the more advanced branches of it, such as mathematical physics, and that the notion is a relic of a primitive, anthropo-

11

morphic interpretation of the various changes occurring in the world. It is beyond serious doubt that the term "cause" rarely if ever appears in the research papers or treatises currently published in the natural sciences, and the odds are heavily against any mention in any book on theoretical physics. Nevertheless, though the *term* may be absent, the *idea* for which it stands continues to have wide currency. It not only crops up in everyday speech, and in investigations into human affairs by economists, social psychologists, and historians, it is also pervasive in the accounts natural scientists give of their laboratory procedures, as well as in the interpretations offered by many theoretical physicists of their mathematical formalism. Descriptions of laboratory procedures refer to changes produced by the operations of various instruments, as well as by human agents, and are unavoidably couched in causal language. Similarly, attempts to understand a physical theory not simply as a self-contained system of formal operations but as statements about physical processes involve obvious causal connotations. For example, in explaining some basic ideas of quantum mechanics, a distinguished physicist writes as follows: "If we want to look at the detailed structure of the orbit of an electron, we must use light waves with a very small wave length. Such light, however, has a high frequency and is a big energy quantum. When it hits the electron, it will knock it out of the orbit and destroy the very object of our examination." In this interpretation of a theoretical formula, intended not only for the man in the street, but also for some of his professional colleagues, the writer employs the expressions "hits," "knocks it out," and "destroys the . . . object"— expressions that certainly signify one familiar type of causal action. The notion of causality, though not necessarily the word "cause," is also present when scientists distinguish in various inquiries between spurious and genuine correlations. In short, the idea of cause is not as outmoded in modern science as is sometimes alleged.

However this may be, explicit discussions of causality usually occur when developments in some branch of science create doubts about the adequacy of habitually employed procedures of inquiry. Let me briefly note three kinds of occasions that may stimulate such reflection. (i) Innovations in scientific theory or techniques of analysis may produce serious disagreements on whether they really contribute to the explanation of certain phenomena. In consequence, assumed requirements for "satisfactory" explanations come to be reconsidered, among others, the question whether explanations must be "causal" and, if so, in what sense. (ii) An explanatory theory in some branch of science may be discovered to lack, or to seem to lack, the power to predict certain kinds of phenomena. This discovery may lead to an analysis of the conditions under which explanations also have predictive force, and in particular to an examination of the question whether explanations must formulate relations of causal dependence if they are to serve as instruments of prediction. (iii) Goal-directed, or teleological, behavior is a pervasive feature of animate processes, especially of human conduct. But despite the fact that the "objective" methods of science have been successfully used in studying various traits of such processes, proposals to extend the use of those methods are often a stimulus to discussions of the question whether teleological behavior (in particular, the individual and social actions of men) can be explained in causal terms. I would like in this paper to say something about problems concerning the use of causal notions that arise in these three contexts of analysis.

II

The first issue I want to consider is whether satisfactory explanations in the sciences are coextensive with those that are causal, in some reasonable sense of the term. However, scientific explanations differ among themselves in a variety of ways, even when they are all proposed answers to such questions as "Why did a certain event occur?" or "Why does a certain relation between events or traits of things hold?" It is therefore desirable to distinguish several types of explanations. Explanations can be classified in any number of ways—for example, on the basis of the subject matters with which they deal, the variables that play a primary role in them, the degree of comprehensiveness they possess, and so on. The classification I will adopt is in terms of certain formal characteristics that explanations exhibit. The four types I will describe are undoubtedly not exhaustive, but they are most frequently exemplified in the sciences with which I have some familiarity.

The first type has been recognized since Aristotle. In it, the statement of what is to be explained (called the *explanandum*), whether it is a singular one formulating a particular occurrence or a universal one formulating an invariable connection of attributes, follows logically or necessarily from some set of initial assumptions (the explanatory premises, called collectively the *explanans*). Explanations of this type thus have a deductive pattern. It has often been assumed that this pattern is the ideal toward which all scientific effort is directed in the search for explanations, since the aim of science is not simply to discover facts, but to show that the discoveries are *reasoned facts* by exhibiting them as necessary consequences of explanatory premises. However, in deductive explanations the premises must state the conditions that are logically sufficient for the truth of what is being explained. One might ask, for example, why a particular piece of ice is floating in a given glass of water on a given occasion. A trivial deductive explanation might be: All ice floats in water; the object in question is a piece of ice; the object therefore floats. Moreover, if the further question is raised why all ice floats in water, it also can be answered by a deductive explanation in which the universal statement about the floating property of ice is shown to be the logical consequence of certain more inclusive principles of physics, such as Archimedes' law about buoyancy. There can be no doubt that very many scientific explanations take a deductive form, especially those found in theoretical treatises, where the task is to account for either strictly universal or statistical laws rather than for some given occurrence on some particular date.

But I must hasten to my second type of explanation. Despite frequent claims that all explanations must be of the first type if they are to be satisfactory, the explanations actually available in many areas of inquiry are rarely of this form. Indeed, most students in certain branches of science, as far as the actual evidence shows, do not even aim at achieving strictly deductive explanations. This is usually, though not exclusively, the case in those studies in which the primary task is to account for specific happenings, such as the occurrence of an avalanche on a given mountainside at a stated time, or the performance of a specified act by a particular person on a given occasion. Although explanations of such individual happenings are sometimes represented to have a deductive pattern, the explanatory premises in them rarely state the sufficient conditions for the occurrences being explained, so that the explanations do not in fact exhibit a deductive form.

The point I want to stress is that we seldom have enough information to state explicitly the full set of sufficient conditions for the occurrence of concrete events. The most we can hope to accomplish in such situations is to state what are at best only "important" indispensable conditions, such that if they are realized the occurrence of the designated events is made "probable"; and we thereby take for granted that the remaining conditions essential for the occurrence of the events are also realized, even when we don't know what those remaining conditions are. For example, in many cases we may introduce the familiar *ceteris paribus* clause into the premises of our explanations—a clause that cloaks our ignorance, but does not permit us to deduce the explanandum. In short, there are widely accepted explanations in science as well as in daily life that do not exhibit a deductive pattern, and in which the explanandum can be inferred from the premises only with some degree of probability. Although I cannot discuss just what is to be understood by "probability" and must assume that it can be given a reasonably definite meaning, I will call such explanations "probabilistic." My second type of scientific explanations contains the probabilistic ones.

A third type of explanation, frequently encountered in the study of human affairs as well as in biology, attempts to account for goal-directed or "purposive" behavior. Such explanations have a prima facie distinctive pattern, apparently quite unlike those classified under the first two types, which for convenience of reference I call "teleological" or "functional." As in explanations of the first two types, however, the explanandum may be a singular or a general statement. On the other hand, a teleological explanation attempts to account for the presence of some object or for certain features of its behavior in terms of the contributions the object and its behavior make toward maintaining some system to which the object belongs in a specified "state" or progression of states. There is time to mention only one simple example of such explanations. The question, "Why do human beings have kidneys?" can be understood as a request for an explanation of the development of that organ in the human species, and perhaps for a physico-chemical account of the formation of the organ in the individual human body. But it can also be understood as a request for a teleological explanation. Such an explanation describes the function performed by the organ in regulating the chemical composition of the blood, and thereby accounts for the presence of kidneys by exhibiting the role they play in maintaining the vital activities of the entire organism. I will have more to say about teleological explanations presently.

The fourth type of explanation includes what are commonly called genetic explanations. Although they closely resemble explanations of the second type in many respects, genetic explanations differ from probabilistic ones in one important feature, as the following example will make clear. As is well known, Mussolini opposed Hitler's attempt to annex Austria in 1934, but approved the annexation in 1938. Why did Mussolini change his mind? The explanation is usually given by historians in the form of a narrative in which the events leading up to this change are recounted, where the events cited are claimed to be causally relevant to what is being explained. Nevertheless, the explanandum does not follow deductively from the explanatory premises—not even if all the tacit assumptions are made explicit—so that the explanation is a probabilistic one. On the other hand, the initial conditions to which historians apply their tacitly assumed general laws (unlike the initial conditions in probabilistic explanations already discussed) refer to events that occurred at widely distributed times rather than simultaneously. This is the distinctive feature of genetic explanations—the use of statements of initial conditions that require mention of sequentially ordered events occurring at different times. Historians cannot account for the change in Mussolini's attitude toward Hitler's actions in Austria by citing, as is commonly done in physics, only data about events that occurred at just one instant of time; they must include in their explanatory premises information concerning what happened at a number of distinct times. Genetic explanations are common in all historical inquiry, not only in the study of human history, and occupy a prominent place in the biological sciences. Evolutionary theory, for example, has the overall pattern of a genetic explanation. The theory accounts for the formation and present diversity of organic species in terms of a series of happenings, many of which did not (indeed, could not) occur at the same time, and could not have been stated until earlier members in the series had already occurred.

III

With these four types of scientific explanation in mind, let me return to the question of whether in explanations generally admitted to be satisfactory and belonging to any of these types, the premises contain causal statements. The word "cause" is highly ambiguous, and some of its current meanings must be noted if the question is to be discussed profitably.

The word "cause" has a legal origin, and is derived from ancient Greek and Roman technical terms denoting actions accountable for wrongs for which there were legal remedies. This use was eventually extended by analogy to cover matters other than human actions, so that the cause of an occurrence is often taken to be anything which is believed to be either partly or wholly "responsible" for that occurrence. However, even if this generic but vague meaning is implicit in all uses of the word, the specific sense associated with the term varies considerably. In some contexts it signifies the *presence* of something, as when a lighted match is said to be the cause of an explosion. In other contexts the word designates the *absence* of something, as when vitamin C deficiency is held to be the cause of scurvy, or lack of rain is said to be the cause of a crop failure. In still other contexts the word denotes the set of initial conditions that are needed when applying universal laws to particular cases, where the laws formulate relations of dependence between variables such that the time-rate of change in one variable is a function of the other variables. For example, a well-known law of physics asserts that the time-rate of change in the distance traversed by a freely falling body is proportional to the time of fall. To apply the law to a particular case, one must specify both the initial position and the initial velocity of the body. Since the initial position and velocity of the body (called its initial state) uniquely determine its later positions and velocities, the state of the system at one time is often said to be the cause of each of its subsequent states.

This brief and incomplete list of senses of the word "cause" makes evident that there is no uniquely correct explication of the term. Accordingly, we must not assume that the word has a precise meaning common to its various uses. The moral to which all this points is that it is a mistake to rule out as illegitimate the use of "cause" in some indicated sense in one domain, on the alleged ground that the term is not used in this sense in another domain, just as it is a mistake to make the sense of term as determined by its use in one domain paradigmatic for its use in all other domains. At any rate, it seems to me futile to discuss whether certain things can, while other things cannot, be "properly" said to be causes. Nevertheless, much energy continues to be devoted to such questions. For example, some influential writers have denied that any of the dispositional traits commonly ascribed to living or inanimate systems (such as irascibility or fragility) can ever be counted as causes. Similarly, other students have disputed the intelligibility of maintaining that the instantaneous state of a body is the cause of another instantaneous state. But such disputes are as idle as were the debates that used to be held over the question whether irrational and imaginary numbers, since they are not cardinal integers, can properly be called "numbers" or whether properties like density and temperature, which cannot be decomposed into additive parts, can correctly be said to be "measurable." It is surely far more profitable to begin with the fact that the word "cause" is not univocal, and then to classify and clarify (as was done with the terms "number" and "measure") the senses in which the term is employed in various contexts.

Let me therefore return briefly to one sense, noted earlier, in which the term is commonly used in practical affairs of daily life. In these contexts, interest in causes is directed to identifying specific but partial determinants of concrete events; and what is generally referred to as "the cause" of an event is a particular occurrence (often, though not invariably, involving an overt manipulation of things by human beings) such that without it the event would not have taken place. The following are examples of such causal statements: the snow fall on December 12 tied up the transportation in New York City; the lights went on when Mrs. Smith turned the switch; the bank failed because of baseless rumors about its solvency. It is evident that the statements are all singular, rather than general or lawlike. Moreover, in none of them is the occurrence tacitly assumed to be "the cause" a *sufficient* condition for the event alleged to be its effect. For example, turning a switch does not suffice to produce illumination, since many other conditions must be satisfied for this to happen. In making such causal statements, it is, of course, possible that we know what these further conditions are, and take them for granted without mentioning them explicitly; but this is rarely the case, and we are usually able to cite only a few of those conditions, without knowing all of them. In either case, what we are doing is designating as *the* cause of an event just one item, selected from what is tacitly supposed to be its full complement of necessary and sufficient conditions, because the item is deemed important for various reasons.

Two further points should be noted about this notion of cause. It takes for granted certain common-sense distinctions concerning the ways events may be ordered, and it assumes that a cause not only precedes its effect but is also spatio-temporally "contiguous" with it. However, no precise criteria exist for deciding when events are contiguous, and the question is usually settled more or less arbitrarily. It is therefore evident that when these common-sense distinctions are inoperative, as in inquiries in which the mathematical definition of continuity is employed in formulating relations of dependence, this notion of cause is also inapplicable.

Second, although in the sense of "cause" under discussion the cause of an event is a *necessary* (or indispensable) condition for its occurrence, the necessity may be only relative. For example, the bank mentioned earlier might not have failed on the day it did, if there had not been false rumors about its financial stability. But banks have been known to fail in the absence of such rumors —indeed, even the bank in question might have failed on some other occasion without the rumors. In short, there may be more than one set of sufficient conditions for an event's occurrence (though the sets may be overlapping). In consequence, if the rumors were the cause of the bank's failure on a specified date, they were an indispensable condition for the failure only on the assumption that (i) the rumors belonged to one set of sufficient conditions for the failure, and (ii) except for the rumors the other conditions in this set were already realized, so that with the circulation of the rumors all the conditions in the set were fulfilled. Accordingly, in the sense of "cause" under discussion, the cause of an event is in general neither a sufficient nor an absolutely necessary condition for the event's occurrence. The cause may be called a "contingently necessary" condition, and satis-fies the following requirement: Suppose E is an event that happened at some specified time t; S is a set of conditions sufficient for the occurrence of E at time t; and C is one of the conditions in S. Although we may not know what conditions other than C are in S, we nevertheless assume that with the occurrence of C all the conditions in S are realized (so that the event E takes place at time t), but that unless C had occurred E would not have occurred at t. C is then said to be a contingently necessary condition for E's occurrence at time t—that is, if the conditions in S other than

C are realized, the event E happens at t if and only if the condition C is also fulfilled.

IV

The question whether scientific explanations are causal can therefore be answered only if it is first made determinate, by indicating in which of the many specific senses of "causal" the question is to be understood. But even after the question is made determinate much remains to be done, for an adequate answer requires a thorough sampling of the various laws and theories that serve as premises in each of the four types of explanation listed above. Both tasks are far beyond the scope of this paper, and I must restrict myself to brief comments on several kinds of law that frequently appear in explanatory premises.

One type of law simply states that a "natural kind" or "substance" exists, as when it is said that there is a mineral called rock salt or a biological species known as *Homo sapiens*. Although philosophers seldom cite them as examples of laws, such statements have the generality that distinguishes conventional scientific laws, for they implicitly assert that every object of a certain kind possesses a characteristic set of invariably conjoined properties. To say, for example, that there is a mineral called rock salt is to say, among other things, that there are objects that exhibit a cubic, crystalline form, are colorless, and have a certain density, melting point, and degree of hardness. Laws of this type do not assert relations of causal dependence in any established sense of "causal." They nevertheless occur in the premises of many primitive explanations. For example, the fact that a given object is harder than talc is explained on an elementary level by noting that the object is a diamond and that diamond is harder than talc. It is admittedly not an explanation typical of the more advanced sciences, and it leaves unanswered the obvious question why diamond is harder than talc. But it is an explanation nonetheless, although clearly not causal.

A second type of law often used as an explanatory premise formulates relations of sequential dependence, and includes many laws that are generally classified as causal. One example of such a law asserts that if a spark is passed through a mixture of hydrogen and oxygen, its passage is followed by the disappearance of the gases and the formation of water vapor. Accordingly, an explanation of some particular occurrence in terms of this law is a causal explanation. However, not all laws of this second type are causal, for there are developmental laws asserting sequential orders of dependence that do not formulate causal relations. One example of such a noncausal developmental law is the statement that the formation of the circulatory system in the human embryo always precedes the formation of the lungs.

A third type of law states a statistical or probabilistic relation between attributes. One such law asserts that in the offspring of human parents both of whom have type *AB* blood, 50 per cent belong to blood group *AB*, 25 per cent to blood group *A*, and the remainder to blood group *B*. Although this law involves assumptions that would generally be regarded as causal (e.g., that the offspring are the product of mating), it does not state a causal relation in any established sense. However, there are statistical laws that would usually be classified as causal, for example, the law that if a human being is vaccinated against smallpox, the probability of his being immune to the disease is greater for one year than it is for four years. Accordingly, while some explanations using laws of this type in their premises are causal, others are not.

The final type of law asserts relations of functional dependence. A familiar example is the Boyle-Charles Law, according to which the product of the pressure and volume of an ideal gas is proportional to its temperature. As formulated, the law simply asserts a certain concomitance in the variation of the specified attributes of a gas, and is therefore generally regarded as making no causal statement. However, as was mentioned earlier, there are also laws of functional dependence that are commonly said to be causal ones, especially laws that state how the time-rate of change in one variable is related to other variables—for example, the familiar law of mechanics according to which the time-rate of change in the momentum of a body depends on the impressed forces acting on it. It is therefore evident that explanations with this type of law in their premises may be either causal or noncausal.

The general conclusion suggested by this hasty survey, namely, that scientific explanations are not uniformly causal, even if allowance is made for the diverse senses in which the term is currently employed—leads directly to the further question whether reliable prediction is possible only in those cases in which the causal determinants of events have been established. The question involves complex issues, but I can deal with it here only in summary fashion.

We can often make successful predictions on the basis of known sequential regularities between events, even though the sequential relations are not directly causal or, at any rate, are not known to be causal. For example, in using a barometer to foretell the weather we do not suppose that a drop in the mercury column is the cause of the subsequent change in weather, whether or not we have grounds for believing that some causal mechanism relates the events indirectly. Similarly, we often predict the coming of an illness on the basis of some early symptom, although we may not know anything about the etiology of the disease. In short, knowledge of causes is not a necessary condition for successful prediction.

But is such knowledge a sufficient condition for prediction? Here the answer varies with the sense of "cause" presupposed by the question. If the term is understood to signify the sufficient (or necessary and sufficient) condition for an event's occurrence, it is a truism that events can always be foretold when their causes are known. However, as has already been noted, the sufficient conditions for the occurrence of specific events are rarely if ever known, so the truism does not carry us very far. On the other hand, if the term is taken to denote some contingently necessary condition for an event, knowledge of its cause does frequently enable us to foretell the event. But even in this case we may be mistaken in believing that the other members of the set of sufficient conditions to which the cause belongs are in fact present, or we may be ignorant of just what those other members are. This last possibility seems to be illustrated more often in the life sciences than in others, in part because many of their explanatory laws are statistical in form whose statistical parameters can rarely be assigned precise values. For example, current evolutionary theory offers a causal explanation for the emergence of biological species. But although it specifies the various changes that must occur if a new species is to emerge, in general we know little about the probabilities with which such changes take place in nature, and we are therefore unable to predict effectively just when a new species will be formed. The conclusion I draw from all this is that knowledge of causes is not co-extensive with ability to predict.

5

I want, finally, to comment briefly on the familiar contrast between causal and teleological explanations, and to sketch arguments for two points: despite its general disrepute in modern science, the notion of teleology is neither hopelessly archaic nor necessarily a mark of superstition; and teleological explanations are fully compatible with causal accounts. Perhaps the chief reason why most contemporary natural scientists disown teleology, and are disturbed by the use of teleological language in the natural sciences, is that the notion is equated with the belief that future events are active agents in their own realization. Such a belief is undoubtedly a species of superstition; but it is not implied by the notion of teleology I wish to defend. The notion I do want to defend is employed in both the physical and biological sciences, whenever some component part or process in a self-regulating system is explained by exhibiting its role in maintaining the system in a specified operative condition. Teleological explanations of this sort account for a component in terms of the *consequences* for a given system resulting from the presence of the component. On the other hand, causal explanations account for the occurrence or maintenance of some feature of a system in terms of *antecedent* events or processes. In the former case, the component's presence has an indefinite number of consequences, but only a selected few of them count as the termini of its activities; in the latter case, the feature has an indefinite number of preceding events or processes, although only some of them are selected as the origins of its occurrence. Accordingly, if teleological explanations are rejected as illegitimate on the ground that by concentrating on the functions of a component they are ignoring all but a selected few of its consequences, by parity of reasoning causal explanations should also be rejected—since by focusing on the origins of some feature characterizing a system they too are ignoring all but a selected handful of the events preceding the feature's occurrence.

However, teleological explanations are not always appropriate. It is appropriate to give such explanations for the motions of a governor on a donkey engine or the operations of kidneys in living organisms, but it makes no sense to explain in this way the motions of the planets or the Babinski reflex in infants. The reason for this is transparent: the engine is self-regulative with respect to its speed of rotation, but the planetary system is not self-maintaining with respect to any of its known features. More generally, some systems of bodies are teleonomic (that is, they continue to operate in certain specified ways despite adverse environmental changes, because they are provided with identifiable mechanisms that can compensate within limits for such changes), but other systems are not; and teleological explanations make good sense only when proposed in connection with teleonomic systems. Accordingly, teleological explanations are more frequent in the biological than in the physical sciences, not because the former are less advanced than are the latter, but simply because living organisms are teleonomic with respect to some of their attributes while most physical systems are not. Nevertheless, as the example of the donkey engine suggests, a teleological account of some element in a system can often be formulated in purely physico-chemical terms and, in any case, does not differ in its verifiable content from a causal explanation of the same facts. Indeed, a teleological explanation can always be transformed into a causal one, even if the causal explanation thereby obtained is relatively primitive. Thus, to explain the human kidneys teleologically by saying that the human body has them in order to keep the blood in a certain chemical state is tantamount to making the causal statement that unless men had kidneys the chemical equilibrium of their blood would not be preserved. Although their scope is restricted to self-maintaining systems, teleological explanations are not incompatible with causal ones, and are no more anthropomorphic than are causal accounts.

Since teleological statements can be verified in the same way and to the same extent as causal statements, the grounds on which the validity of statements of either type can be assessed is also the same. Nevertheless, the logic governing such assessments, especially in domains in which relevant experiments or other forms of controlled empirical analysis cannot be performed, is often obscure. In particular, it is far from clear what rules for weighing evidence are used by historians when they accept one causal explanation rather than another for specific human actions. For example, assuming as well established fact that the Puritan passengers on the *Mayflower* wanted not only to practice their religious beliefs but also to improve their fortunes, what is the rationale historians employ for assigning causal efficacy to one rather than another of these factors in their explanation of the founding of the Massachusetts colony? The example illustrates an important but unresolved class of methodological problems. Much of the obscurity that continues to envelop them could, I am convinced, be removed, if philosophers concerned with the logic of inquiry addressed themselves to those problems not singlehanded, but in collaboration with men actively engaged in empirical research. Let me therefore conclude this paper with an expression of my hope that such collaboration will soon be undertaken.

DISCUSSION

Types of Causal Explanation in Science

QUESTION: I would like to ask your definition of teleology—because not all the examples that you quoted I, as a biologist, would have called teleological.

NAGEL: Obviously such a definition is in part an arbitrary matter. I would say that a system is teleological if it has a mechanism which enables it to maintain a specific property despite environmental changes. Hence my paradigm example, the ability of the human body to maintain the internal temperature of its blood despite extreme changes of external temperatures.

QUESTION: Could a computer be a teleological system under certain conditions?

NAGEL: It might be. I think it is possible to state fairly precisely under what conditions a system is teleological. It must have certain types of compensating mechanisms—what we call essentially a negative feedback. I do not mean by my definition that systems that are self-maintaining in a very obvious and naïve sense would be called teleological, where others would not. For example, I would not say that a simple pendulum which moves in such a way that it strives to achieve the lowest potential energy is a teleological system. There are no compensating effects in the pendulum. Hence, as a system, it does not have an internal structure that enables it to compensate for environmental changes.

QUESTION: Would you say that if you define a teleological system as one in which the whole explains the part rather than the part the whole, then systems that historically have been called teleological by philosophers turn out to be self-maintained systems? This seems to me probably true, and it suggests that there may have been some grain of truth in the old notion of teleological explanation.

NAGEL: It might very well be, but I would not define a teleological system or teleological explanation as one that explains the part in terms of the whole. Rather, a teleological explanation in my sense would be one that indicates the role a part plays in the maintenance of some characteristic in the whole system. Apart from that, it might be that those systems that have been so characterized by tradition on analysis turn out to be teleological systems in my sense. The question is whether one can distinguish, perhaps not with utmost precision, but at least roughly, between systems that are self-maintaining and systems that are not. If I may just add one comment, one of my difficulties with the use of teleological notions in social science has been that, whereas in the case of organic systems there is a clear sense in which one can say a system is no longer self-maintaining with respect to some specific character, many of the writings in the area of social inquiry about functional or teleological systems do not make clear under what conditions a system is not self-maintained. One obvious sense, of course, would be when the systems are destroyed, but societies on the whole are destroyed only when the members are decimated, which is not quite the sense that is relevant here.

QUESTION: May I ask you to comment on one other point within this general area? One connotation of the word "teleological" is what we ordinarily think of as purposive, or in the more or less subjective sense, goal-directed, behavior. Social scientists employ this kind of teleology when they ask people what they are intending to do and then use the statement of intention as an explanatory factor in interpreting the actual course of events. Where would you place this particular type of teleology in your more general scheme?

NAGEL: That does not present any special problem to me. If one were to think of an individual's striving toward some goal in the sense of something specific he intends to do, his intention is a variable, as in biology, for example, the activity of the adrenal gland would be a variable. If his intention is something that contributes to the maintenance of some specific characteristic of the individual, it is on a par with any other factor that you might isolate for study as possibly contributing to the maintenance. Also, I think one ought to add that the important, difficult, technical questions always arise when we try to explain the mechanism by means of which the various factors or variables are related to one another in terms of how a change in one is compensated by a change in the other. These are details which obviously require a great deal of empirical and theoretical research. Merely to assert that there are such compensating effects without tracing through the mechanism by means of which they are effected is only the beginning of wisdom. It is my impression that there often is not enough attention paid to isolating the variables in so-called social systems or social institutions for study from the point of view of understanding their functions, of understanding just what the mechanism is by which they are related. I think that in the social sciences such inquiry is not as far advanced as in some other disciplines.

QUESTION: I was not surprised by your remark that you find a special difficulty in historical explanation because what you have given us is not the theory of historical explanation. You have defined cause as a nonsufficient condition intervening among many conditions and provoking certain events. More closely, you define cause as the factor without which the phenomenon which you try to explain would not have happened. But that is exactly the definition which Max Weber used for the definition of historical cause. What historians are doing is exactly what you have described. Namely, among many conditions they take one which, in their minds, is more or less responsible (with a rather vague meaning of the word "responsible") for the events they are trying to explain. The difficulty you have shown us was largely created by your own example of a pure motive, which no serious historian would do.

NAGEL: I must beg to differ on this last point. It seems to me that historians do make causal imputations, causal descriptions, simply on the basis of having established the fact that an individual possesses some characteristic or has performed some action. Let me, if I may, restate my problem. My problem is how to distinguish, and how to avoid in historical inquiry, the obvious fallacy of *post hoc*. Where repetition is possible, we can check this. In the historical case it is certainly more difficult to do this. My impression is that historians have been rather slapdash in their imputation of causal significance without taking account of the *post hoc* fallacy.

QUESTION: I am not sure a good historian would say that Antony did leave the battlefield because he was in love with Cleopatra. I feel that the logic is rather different. They are trying to give a nonrational reason for a nonrational action which is known. But such reasons can never be known for sure, because nobody knows motives exactly. I believe it is a different type of explanation than purely historical research of cause.

NAGEL: The example that I used was obviously an example of an individual action, but I think my problem would be the same used with aggregative action. In accounting for occurrences such as the French Revolution, historians say that some action often is *a* cause or *the* cause or an *important* cause. It seems to me that historians have rarely asked themselves what they mean when they say that something is the most important cause. Even conceptual clarification has not been carried through by historians, to say nothing of their trying to find the evidence which would substantiate their claim. This is my problem, not the particular example.

QUESTION: How do you regard Max Weber's solution of your problem?

NAGEL: I certainly have learned a lot from Max Weber. But remember, Max Weber tries to answer this simply by saying, perform a mental experiment. This may be the best we can do at the moment, but I would like to think that we can do a little bit better.

QUESTION: When you said that the cause was not a sufficient condition, but was one without which the event would not happen, it was difficult for me to see why this was not exactly what one means by a necessary condition. I have the problem of just how to decide which of the accompanying circumstances might, or might not, have been there if the circumstance looked upon as a cause was not there. I can't see any lack of symmetry between necessary and sufficient.

NAGEL: It is not a sufficient condition because it alone would not yield the outcome; and it is not necessary because I am allowing for the possibility that there may be more than one set of sufficient conditions. Suppose the event E might—this is purely hypothetical—have two sets of sufficient conditions for its occurrence, namely A and B. Then suppose that alpha is an element in A and that A-alpha is the remaining set of conditions. But the event could have happened not because of A but because of B. It would not be correct to say that a necessary condition for the event E is the occurrence of alpha, since alpha need not have occurred if alpha is not a constituent of the second set of conditions B.

QUESTION: I find myself a little worried about the teleological definition. You take as an example the self-regulator of the animal body. This involves a very small range of temperature, humidity, and such things. All these are conditions of nature which a primitive man could not have met. Man now meets them with all sorts of other things that have been put around man in order to make the self-regulator still self-regulating. Now if that is true, and I think it is, then what could be done about social problems with this same narrrow limitation that there is upon man's thermal control?

NAGEL: Of course the range in which the organism is self-maintaining might differ with respect to different characteristics. The body might maintain its temperature only within a narrow range. With respect to maintaining the circulation of the blood, environmental changes might be very limited. For each particular characteristic there might be a different range within which the body is self-maintaining. In a social system—to the extent that one can specify what it is, what the characteristics are, and what the elements are that contribute to its self-maintenance—I think the analysis would operate in the same way but the substantive variables would be different.

QUESTION: You report several different types of accounts or causal explanations and are wondering if any of these, or several of these, might be used for the same event. Or, is it that you think certain types of explanation are important to certain kinds of events?

For example, I am not sure I would compare a genetic account with a teleological account or a probabilistic account of the same events.

NAGEL: I am not sure I know how to answer that question. In general, my inclination would be to say in certain identifiable situations one sense of cause is appropriate because this is the way people do use it. My attention was brought to this by reading a recent book by H. L. A. Hart and A. M. Honoré, *Causality and the Law*. There the problem is the extent to which an individual is liable for certain tortuous actions in a sequence for which he was in some way causally responsible. One point the authors make is that, in the law, the word "cause" is used in the sense I have tried to specify. When a judge decides that an individual is liable to a certain amount (in money payment or prison term) for an action he has caused, it is this sense of cause that is presumably relevant. It would make a very good case for review to analyze this sense of cause in terms of, let us say, the idea of irregularity. My inclination would be to say that in terms of linguistic behavior, in terms of what people say they mean, this seems to be the appropriate sense of cause. To be sure, my analogy tends to include other things as well. I am not sure I have answered the question.

Cause and Effect in Biology

Ernst Mayr

BEING a practicing biologist I cannot attempt the kind of analysis of cause and effect in biological phenomena that a logician would undertake. I will, instead, concentrate on the special difficulties encountered by the classical concept of causality in biology. From the first attempts to achieve a unitary concept of cause, the student of causality has been bedeviled by them. Descartes' grossly mechanistic interpretation of life, and the logical extreme to which his ideas were carried by Holbach and de la Mettrie, inevitably provoked the vitalistic theories that have been in vogue, off and on, to the present day. I have only to mention names like Driesch (Entelechie), Bergson (*élan vital*), and Lecomte de Noüy, among the more prominent authors of the recent past. Though these authors may differ in particulars, they all agree in claiming that living beings and life processes cannot be causally explained in terms of physical and chemical phenomena. It is our task to ask whether this assertion is justified, and if we answer this question with "no," to determine the source of the misunderstanding.

Causality, no matter how it is defined in terms of logic, is believed to contain three elements:

1. an explanation of past events ("*a posteriori* causality");
2. prediction of future events; and
3. the interpretation of teleological, that is "goal directed," phenomena.

Explanation, prediction, and teleology must be the cardinal points in any discussion of causality and were quite rightly singled out as such by Dr. Nagel. Biology can make a significant contribution to all three of them. But before I can discuss this contribution in detail, I must say a few words about biology as a science.

33

BIOLOGY

The word "biology" suggests a uniform and unified science. Yet recent developments have made it increasingly clear that biology is a most complex area, indeed, that "biology" is a label for two largely separate fields which differ greatly in method, *Fragestellung*, and basic concepts. Beyond the level of purely descriptive structural biology, one finds two very different areas, which may be designated as *functional biology* and *evolutionary biology*. To be sure, the two fields have many points of contact and overlap. Any biologist, working in one of these fields, must have a knowledge and appreciation of the other if he wants to avoid the label of narrow-minded specialist. Yet in his own research he will be occupied with problems of either one or the other field. We cannot discuss cause and effect in biology without first having characterized these two fields.

Functional Biology

The functional biologist is vitally concerned with the operation and interaction of structural elements, from molecules up to organs and whole individuals. His perpetual question is: "How?" How does something operate, how does it function? The functional anatomist who studies an articulation shares this method and approach with the molecular biologist who studies the function of a DNA molecule in the transfer of genetic information. The functional biologist attempts to isolate the particular component he studies, and in any given study he usually deals with a single individual, a single organ, a single cell, or a single part of a cell. He attempts to eliminate, or control, all variables and he repeats his experiments under constant or varying conditions until he believes he has clarified the function of the element he studies. The chief technique of the functional biologist is the experiment and his approach is essentially the same as that of the physicist and chemist. Indeed, by isolating the studied phenomenon sufficiently from the complexities of the organism, he may achieve the ideal of a purely physical or chemical experiment. In spite of certain limitations of this method, one must agree with the functional biologist that such a simplified approach is an absolute necessity to achieve his particular objectives. The spectacular success of biochemical and biophysical research justifies this direct, although distinctly simplistic approach.

Evolutionary biology

The evolutionary biologist differs in his method and in the problems in which he is interested. His basic question is: "Why?" When we say "why" we must always be aware of the ambiguity of this term. It may mean "How come?" but it may also mean the finalistic "What for?" It is obvious that the evolutionist has in mind the historical "How come?" when he asks "Why?" Every organism, whether individual or species, is the product of a history that dates back more than 2,000 million years. As Max Delbrück (1949) has said, "a mature physicist, acquainting himself for the first time with the problems of biology, is puzzled by the circumstance that there are no 'absolute phenomena' in biology. Everything is time-bound and space-bound. The animal or plant or microorganism he is working with is but a link in an evolutionary chain of changing forms, none of which has any permanent validity." There is hardly any structure or function in an organism that can be fully understood unless studied on this historical background. To find the causes for the existing characteristics, and particularly adaptations, of organisms is the main preoccupation of the evolutionary biologist. He is impressed by the enormous diversity of the organic world. He wants to know the reasons for this diversity as well as the pathway by which it has been achieved. He studies the forces that bring about changes in faunas and floras (as in part documented by paleontology), and he studies the steps by which have evolved the miraculous adaptations so characteristic of every aspect of the organic world.

We can use the language of information theory to attempt still another characterization of these two fields of biology. The functional biologist deals with all aspects of the decoding of the programmed information contained in the DNA program of the zygote. The evolutionary biologist, on the other hand, is interested in the history of these programs of information and in the laws that control the changes of these programs from generation to generation. In other words, he is interested in the causes of these changes.

Many of the old arguments of biological philosophy can be stated far more precisely in terms of these genetic programs. For instance, as Schmalhausen, in Russia, and I have pointed out independently, the inheritance of acquired characteristics becomes quite unthinkable when applied to the model of the transfer of genetic information from a peripheral phenotype of the DNA of the germ cells.

But let us not have an erroneous concept of these programs. It is characteristic of these genetic messages that the programming is only in part rigid. Such phenomena as learning, memory, non-genetic structural modification, and regeneration show how "open" these programs are. Yet, even here there is great specificity, for instance with respect to what can be "learned," at what stage in the life cycle, and how long a memory engram is retained. The program, then, may be in part quite unspecific, and yet the range of possible variation is itself included in the specifications of the program. The programs, therefore, are in some respects highly specific; in others they merely specify "reaction norms" or general capacities and potentialities.

Let me illustrate this duality of programs by the difference between two kinds of birds with respect to "species recognition." As you know, the young cowbird is raised by foster parents, let us say, in the nest of a song sparrow or warbler. As soon as it becomes independent from its foster parents, it seeks the company of other young cowbirds, even though it has never seen a cowbird before! In contrast, after hatching from the egg, a young goose will accept as its parent the first moving (and preferably also calling) object it can follow and become "imprinted" to. What is programmed is, in one case, a definite gestalt; in the other, merely the capacity to become imprinted to a gestalt. Similar differences in the specificity of the inherited program are universal throughout the organic world.

Let us now get back to our main topic and ask: Is *cause* the same thing in functional and evolutionary biology?

Max Delbrück, again, has reminded us that as recently as 1870, Helmholtz postulated "that the behavior of living cells should be accountable in terms of motions of molecules acting under certain fixed force laws." Now, says Delbrück correctly, we cannot even account for the behavior of a single hydrogen atom. As he also says, "any living cell carries with it the experiences of a billion years of experimentation by its ancestors."

Let me illustrate the difficulties of the concept of causality in biology by an example. We may ask: What is the cause of bird migration? or, more specifically: Why did the warbler at my summer place in New Hampshire start his southward migration on the night of August 25?

I can list four equally legitimate causes for this migration:

1. *An ecological cause.* The warbler, being an insect eater, must migrate, because it would starve to death during the winter in New Hampshire.

2. *A genetic cause.* The warbler has acquired a genetic constitution in the course of the evolutionary history of his species which induces it to respond appropriately to the proper stimuli from the environment. On the other hand, the screech owl, nesting right next to it, lacks this constitution and does not respond to these stimuli. As a result, it is sedentary.

3. *An intrinsic physiological cause.* The warbler flew south because its migration is tied in with photoperiodism. It responds to the decrease in day length and is ready to migrate as soon as the hours of daylight have dropped below a certain number.

4. *An extrinsic physiological cause.* Finally, the warbler migrated on August 25 because a cold air mass, with northerly winds, passed over our area on that day. The sudden drop in temperature and the associated weather conditions affected the bird, already in a general physiological readiness for migration, so that it actually took off.

Now, if we look over the four causes of the migration of this bird once more, we can readily see an immediate set of causes consisting of the physiological condition of the bird interacting with photoperiodism and drop in temperature. We might call these the *proximate* causes of migration. The other two causes, the lack of food during winter and the genetic disposition of the bird, are the *ultimate* causes. These are causes that have a history and that have been incorporated into the system through many thousands of generations of natural selection. It is evident that the functional biologist would be concerned with analysis of the proximate causes, while the evolutionary biologist would be concerned with analysis of the ultimate causes. This is the case with almost any biological phenomenon we might want to study. There are always proximate causes and ultimate causes; both have to be explained and interpreted for a complete understanding of the given phenomenon.

Still another way to express these differences would be to say that proximate causes govern the responses of the individual (and his organs) to immediate factors of the environment, while ultimate causes are responsible for the evolution of the particular DNA code of information with which every individual of every species is endowed. The logician will, presumably, be little concerned with these distinctions. Yet, the biologist knows that many heated arguments about the "cause" of a certain biological phenomenon could have been avoided if the two opponents had realized that one of them was concerned with a proximate and the other with an ultimate cause. I might illustrate this by a quotation from Loeb (1916): "The earlier writers explained the growth of the legs in the tadpole of the frog or toad as a case of adaptation to life on land. We know through Gudernatsch that the growth of the legs can be produced at any time even in the youngest tadpole, which is unable to live on land, by feeding the animal with the thyroid gland."

Let us now get back to the definition of "cause" in formal philosophy and see how it fits with the usual explanatory "cause" of functional and evolutionary biology. We might, for instance, define cause as: a nonsufficient condition without which an event would not have happened, or as a member of a set of jointly suffi-cient reasons without which the event would not happen (after Scriven MS). Such definitions describe causal relations quite adequately in certain branches of biology, particularly those that deal with chemical and physical unit phenomena. In a strictly formal sense they are also applicable to more complex phenomena, and yet seem to have little operational value in those branches of biology that deal with complex systems. I doubt that there is a scientist who would question the ultimate causality of all biological phenomena, that is, that a causal explanation can be given for past biological events. Yet such an explanation will often have to be so unspecific ˏand purely formal that its explanatory value can certainly be challenged. When dealing with a complex system, an explanation can hardly be considered very illuminating that states: "Phenomenon A is caused by a complex set of interacting factors, one of which is b." Yet this is about all one can often say. We will return to this difficulty in connection with the problem of prediction. However, let us first consider the problem of teleology.

TELEOLOGY

This problem had its begining with Aristotle's classification of causes, one of the categories being the "final" causes. It is based on the observation of the orderly and purposive development of the individual from the egg to the "final" stage, adulthood, and for the development of the whole world from its beginning (chaos?) to its present order. Final cause has been defined as "the cause responsible for the orderly reaching of a preconceived ultimate goal." All goal-seeking behavior has been classified as "teleological," but so have many other phenomena whose goal-seeking nature is questionable.

Aristotelian scholars have rightly emphasized that Aristotle—by training and interest—was first and foremost a biologist and that his preoccupation with biological phenomena dominated his ideas on causes and induced him to postulate final causes in addi-tion to material, formal, and efficient causes. Thinkers from the

time of Aristotle to the present have been challenged by the
apparent contradiction between a mechanistic interpretation of
natural processes and the seemingly purposive sequence of events
in organic growth, in reproduction, and in animal behavior. Such
a rational thinker as Claude Bernard (1885) has stated the paradox
in these words:

> There is, so to speak, a preestablished design of each being and of
> each organ of such a kind that each phenomenon by itself depends upon
> the general forces of nature, but when taken in connection with the
> others it seems directed by some invisible guide on the road it follows
> and led to the place it occupies.
>
> We admit that the life phenomena are attached to physicochemical
> manifestations, but it is true that the essential is not explained thereby;
> for no fortuitous coming together of physicochemical phenomena con-
> structs each organism after a plan and a fixed design (which are
> foreseen in advance) and arouses the admirable subordination and
> harmonious agreement of the acts of life. . . . Determinism can never
> be but physicochemical determinism. The vital force and life belong
> to the metaphysical world.

What is the *x*, this seemingly purposive agent, this "vital force,"
in organic phenomena? It is only in our lifetime that explanations
have been advanced which deal adequately with this paradox.

The many dualistic, finalistic, and vitalistic philosophies of
the past merely replaced the unknown *x* by a different unknown
y or *z*, for calling an unknown factor "entelechia" or *élan vital* is
not an explanation. I shall not waste time showing how wrong most
of these past attempts were. Even though some of the underlying
observations of these conceptual schemes are quite correct, the
supernaturalistic conclusions drawn from these observations are
altogether misleading.

Where, then, is it legitimate to speak of purpose and purposiveness in nature, and where is it not? To this question we can now
give a firm and unambiguous answer. An individual who—to use
the language of the computer—has been "programmed," can act
purposefully. Historical processes, however, *cannot* act purposefully.
A bird that starts its migration, an insect that selects its host plant,

an animal that avoids a predator, a male that displays to a female, all act purposefully because they have been programmed to do so. When I speak of the programmed 'individual," I do so in a broad sense. A programmed computer itself is an "individual" in this sense, but so is, during reproduction, a pair of birds whose instinctive and learned actions and interactions obey, so to speak, a single program.

The completely individualistic and yet also species specific DNA program of every zygote, which controls the development of the central and peripheral nervous systems, of the sense organs, of the hormones, physiology, and morphology, is the *program* for the behavior computer of this individual.

Natural selection does its best to favor the production of programs guaranteeing behavior that increases fitness. A behavior program that guarantees instantaneous, correct reaction to a potential food source, to a potential enemy, or to a potential mate will certainly give greater fitness, in the Darwinian sense, than a program that lacks these properties. A behavior program that allows for appropriate learning and the improvement of behavior reactions by various types of feedbacks again adds more to the probability of survival than a program that lacks these properties.

The purposive action of an individual, as far as it is based on the properties of its genetic program, therefore, is no more nor less purposive than the actions of a computer that has been programmed to respond appropriately to various inputs. It is a purely mechanistic purposiveness.

We biologists have long felt that it is ambiguous to designate such programmed, goal-directed behavior as teleological, because this term has also been used in a very different sense, for the final stage in evolutionary adaptive processes. When Aristotle spoke of final causes, he was particularly concerned with the marvelous adaptations found throughout the plant and animal kingdom. He was concerned with what later authors have called "design" or "plan" in nature. He ascribed to final causes not only "mimicry" or "symbiosis," but all the other adaptations of animals and plants to each other and to their physical environment. The Aristotelians and their successors asked themselves what goal-directed process could have produced such a well-ordered design in nature.

It is now evident that the terms "teleology" and "teleological" have been applied to two entirely different sets of phenomena. On one hand is the production and perfection throughout the history of the animal and plant kingdoms of ever new and ever improved DNA programs of information. On the other hand is the testing of these programs and their decoding throughout the lifetime of each individual. There is a fundamental difference between, end-directed behavioral activities or developmental processes of an individual or system, which are controlled by a program, and the steady improvement of the genetically coded programs. This genetic improvement is evolutionary adaptation controlled by natural selection.

To avoid confusion between the two entirely different types of end-direction, Pittendrigh (1958:394) has introduced the term "teleonomic," as a descriptive term for all end-directed systems, "not committed to Aristotelian teleology." This negative definition not only places the entire burden on the word "system," but it makes no clear distinction between the two teleologies of Aristotle. It would seem useful to rigidly restrict the term teleonomic to systems operating on the basis of a program of coded information. Teleonomy in biology designates "the apparent purposefulness of organisms and their characteristics," as expressed by Julian Huxley (1960).

Such a clear-cut separation of teleonomy, which has an analyzable physiochemical basis, from teleology, which deals more broadly with the overall harmony of the organic world, is most useful because these two entirely different phenomena have so often been confused with each other.

The development or behavior of an individual is purposive, natural selection is definitely not. When McLeod (1957) stated, "What is most challenging about Darwin, however, is his re-introduction of purpose into the natural world," he chose the wrong word. The word "purpose" is singularly inapplicable to evolutionary change, which is, after all, what Darwin was considering. If an organism is well adapted, if it shows superior fitness, this is not because of any purpose of its ancestors or of an outside agency, e.g., "Nature" or "God," who created a superior design or plan. Darwin "has swept out such finalistic teleology by the front door," as Simpson (1960) has rightly said.

We can summarize this discussion by stating that there is no conflict between causality and teleonomy, but that scientific biology has not found any evidence that would support teleology in the sense of various vitalistic or finalistic theories (Simpson 1950, 1960; Koch 1957). All the so-called teleological systems which Dr. Nagel discussed in the last lecture [1] were actually illustrations of teleonomy.

THE PROBLEM OF PREDICTION

The third great problem of causality in biology is that of prediction. In the classical theory of causality the touchstone of the goodness of a causal explanation was its predictive value. This view is still maintained in Bunge's modern classic (1959:307): "A theory can predict to the extent to which it can describe and explain." It is evident that Bunge is a physicist; no biologist would have made such a statement. The theory of natural selection can describe and explain phenomena with considerable precision, but it cannot make reliable predictions, except through such trivial and meaningless circular statements as, for instance: "the fitter individuals will on the average leave more offspring." Scriven (1959) has emphasized quite correctly that one of the most important contributions to philosophy made by the evolutionary theory is that it has demonstrated the independence of explanation and prediction.

Although prediction is not an inseparable concomitant of causality, every scientist is nevertheless happy if his causal explanations simultaneously have high predictive value. We can distinguish many categories of prediction in biological explanation. Indeed, it

[1] Also in his recent book (Nagel, 1961).

is difficult to define "prediction" in biology. A competent zoo-geographer can predict with high accuracy what animals will be found on a previously unexplored mountain range or island. A paleontologist likewise can predict with high probability what kind of fossils can be expected in a newly accessible geological horizon. Is such correct guessing of the results of past events genuine prediction? A similar doubt pertains to taxonomic predictions. The term "prediction" is, however, surely legitimately used for future events. Four examples illustrate the range of predictability:

1. *Prediction in classification.* If I have identified a fruit fly as an individual of *Drosophila melanogaster* on the basis of bristle pattern and the proportions of face and eye, I can predict numerous structural and behavioral characteristics which I will find if I study other aspects of this individual. If I find a new species with the diagnostic key characters of the genus *Drosophila,* I can at once predict a whole set of biological properties.

2. *Prediction of most physicochemical phenomena on the molecular level.* Predictions of very high accuracy can be made with respect to most biochemical unit processes in organisms, such as metabolic pathways, and with respect to biophysical phenomena in simple systems, such as the action of light, heat, and electricity in physiology.

In 1 and 2 the predictive value of causal statements is usually very high. Yet there are numerous other generalizations or causal statements in biology that have low predictive values, for instance:

3. *Prediction of the outcome of complex ecological interactions.* The statement, "An abandoned pasture in southern New England will be replaced by a stand of Grey Birch (*Betula populifolia*) and White Pine (*Pinus strobus*)," is often correct. Even more often, however, the replacement may be an almost solid stand of *Pinus strobus,* or *Pinus strobus* may be replaced by cherry (*Prunus*), red cedar (*Juniperus virginianus*), maple, sumac, and several other species.

Another example also illustrates this unpredictability. When two species of flour beetles, *Tribolium confusum* and *Tribolium castaneum,* are brought together in a uniform environment, sifted wheat flour, one of the two species will always displace the other. At high temperatures and humidities, *Tribulium castaneum* will win out; at low temperatures and humidities, *Tribolium confusum* will be the victor. Under intermediate conditions the outcome is indeterminate [2] and hence unpredictable (Table 1) (Park 1954).

TABLE 1—Two species of *Tribolium* in competition (after Park, 1954)*

Condition	Number of replicas	Victorious species Number of trials	
		confusum	castaneum
34 degrees C., 70 per cent h.	30	—	30
29 degrees C., 70 per cent h.	66	11	55
24 degrees C., 70 per cent h.	30	21	9
34 degrees C., 30 per cent h.	60	53	7
29 degrees C., 30 per cent h.			
24 degrees C., 30 per cent h.	20	20	—

* h = humidity

4. *Prediction of evolutionary events.* Probably nothing in biology is less predictable than the future course of evolution. Looking at the Permian reptiles, who would have predicted that most of the more flourishing groups would become extinct (many rather rapidly) while one of the most undistinguished branches gave rise to the mammals? Which student of the Cambrian fauna would have predicted the revolutionary changes in the marine life of the subsequent geological eras? Unpredictability also characterizes small-scale evolution. Students of natural selection have discovered again and again that independent parallel lines exposed to the same selection pressure will respond at different rates and with different correlated effects, none of them predictable.

As is true in many other branches of science, the validity of predictions for biological phenomena (except a few chemical or physical unit processes) is nearly always statistical. We can predict with high accuracy that slightly more than 500 of the next 1000 newborns will be boys. We cannot predict the sex of a particular unborn child.

[2] In the meantime Lerner and Dempster (1962) have found that the i-determinacy is due to genetic heterogeneity.

REASONS FOR INDERTERMINACY IN BIOLOGY

Without claiming to exhaust all the possible reasons for indeterminacy, I can list four classes. Although they somewhat overlap
each other, each deserves to be treated separately.

1. *Randomness of an event with respect to the significance of the event*

Spontaneous mutation, caused by an error in DNA replication,
illustrates this cause for indeterminacy very well. The occurrence of
a given mutation is in no way related to the evolutionary needs of
the particular organism or of the population to which it belongs.
The precise results of a given selection pressure are unpredictable
because mutation, recombination, and developmental homeostasis
are making indeterminate contributions to the response to this pressure. All the steps in the determination of the genetic contents of
a zygote contain a large component of this type of randomness.
What we have described for mutation is also true for crossing over,
chromosomal segregation, gametic selection, mate selection, and
early survival of the zygotes. The underlying molecular phenomena
as well as the mechanical motions responsible for this randomness
are not related to their biological effects.

2. *Uniqueness of all entities at the higher levels of biological integration*

The uniqueness of biological entities and phenomena is one of
the major differences between biology and the physical sciences.
Physicists and chemists have difficulty understanding the biologist's
stress on the unique, although such an understanding has been
greatly facilitated by the developments in modern physics. If a
physicist says "Ice floats on water," his statement is true for any
piece of ice and any body of water. The members of a class usually

lack the individuality that is so characteristic of the organic world where all individuals are unique, all stages in the life cycle are unique, all populations are unique, all species and higher categories are unique, all inter-individual contacts are unique, all natural associations of species are unique, and all evolutionary events are unique. Where applicable to man, these statements are self-evident. However, they are equally valid for all sexually reproducing animals and plants. Uniqueness, of course, does not entirely preclude prediction. We can make many valid statements about human attributes and human behavior and likewise about other organisms. But most of these statements (except taxonomic ones, see above) have purely statistical validity. Uniqueness is particularly characteristic for evolutionary biology. It is quite impossible to have, for unique phenomena, general laws like those existing in classical mechanics.

3. *Extreme complexity*

The physicist Elsässer stated in a recent symposium: an "outstanding feature of all organisms is their well-nigh unlimited structural and dynamical complexity." This is true. Every organic system is so rich in feedbacks, homeostatic devices, and potential multiple pathways that a complete description is quite impossible. Furthermore, the analysis of such a system would require its destruction and would thus be futile.

4. *Emergence of new qualities at higher levels of integration*

A discussion, in this context, of "emergence" is beyond our scope. All I can do here is to state its principle dogmatically: "When two entities are combined at a higher level of integration, not all the properties of the new entity are necessarily a logical or predictable consequence of the properties of the components." This difficulty is by no means confined to biology, but it is certainly one of the major sources of indeterminacy in biology. Let us remember that indeterminacy does not mean lack of cause, but merely unpredictability.

All four reasons, individually and combined, reduce the precision of prediction. One may raise the question, at this point, whether predictability in classical mechanics and unpredictability in biology are due to a difference of degree or of kind. There is much to suggest that the difference is, to a considerable part, merely of degree. Classical mechanics is at one end of a continuum and biology at the other. Let us take the classical example of the gas laws. They are only statistically true, but the population of molecules in a gas obeying the gas laws is so enormous that the actions of individual molecules become integrated into a predictable, one might say absolute, result. A sample of five or twenty molecules would show definite individuality. The difference in the size of the studied "populations" certainly contributes to the difference between the physical sciences and biology.

CONCLUSIONS

Let us now return to our initial question and try to summarize some of our conclusions on the nature of the cause and effect relations in biology.

(a) Causality in biology is a far cry from causality in classical mechanics.

(b) Explanations of all but the simplest biological phenomena usually consist of sets of causes. This is particularly true for those biological phenomena that can be understood only if their evolutionary history is also considered. Each set is like a pair of brackets which contains much that is unanalyzed and much that can presumably never be analyzed completely.

(c) In view of the high number of multiple pathways possible for most biological processes (except the purely physicochemical ones) and in view of the randomness of many of the biological processes, particularly on the molecular level (as well as for other reasons), causality in biological systems is not predictive, or at best is only statistically predictive.

(d) The existence of complex programs of information in the

DNA of the germ plasm permits teleonomic purposiveness. However, evolutionary research has found no evidence whatsoever for a "goal-seeking" of evolutionary lines, as postulated in that kind of teleology that sees "plan and design" in nature. The harmony of the living universe, so far as it exists, is an *a posteriori* product of natural selection.

Finally, causality in biology is not in real conflict with the causality of classical mechanics. As modern physics has also demonstrated, the causality of classical mechanics is only a very simple, special case of causality. Predictability, for instance, is not a necessary component of causality. The complexities of biological causality do not justify embracing nonscientific ideologies, like vitalism or finalism, but should encourage all those who have been trying to give a broader basis to the concept of causality.

REFERENCES

BERNARD, C. *Leçons sur les phénomènes de la vie.* Vol. 1, 1885

BUNGE, M. *Causality.* Cambridge: Harvard University Press, 1959.

DELBRÜCK, M. "A Physicist Looks at Biology," *Trans. Conn. Acad. Arts & Sci.,* 38 (1949), 173-90.

GLASS, B. "The Relation of the Physical Sciences to Biology—Indeterminacy and Causality," in Bernard Baumrin (ed.), *Philosophy of Science,* New York: Interscience Publishers, John Wiley and Sons, 1963, pp. 223-57.

HUXLEY, J. "The Openbill's Open Bill: A Teleonomic Enquiry," *Zool. Jb. Syst.,* 88 (1960), 9-30.

KOCH, L. F. "Vitalistic-Mechanistic Controversy," *Sci. Monthly,* 85 (1957), 245-55.

LERNER, I. M., and DEMPSTER. "Indeterminism in Interspecific Competition," *Proc. Natl. Acad. Sci. U.S.,* 48 (1962), 821-26.

LOEB, J. *The Organism as a Whole.* New York: G. P. Putnam's Sons, 1916.

McLEOD, R. B. "Teleology and Theory of Human Behavior," *Science,* 125 (1957), 477-80.

NAGEL, E. *The Structure of Science.* New York: Harcourt, Brace & World 1961.

PARK, T. "Experimental Studies of Interspecies Competition. II, Temperature, Humidity, and Competition in Two Species of Tribolium," *Physiol. Zool.,* 27 (1954), 177-238.

PITTENDRIGH, C. S. *In* Roe and Simpson, *Behavior and Evolution.* New Haven: Yale University Press, 1958, pp. 390-416.

SCRIVEN, M. "Explanation and Prediction in Evolutionary Theory," *Science,* 130 (1959), 477-82.

SIMPSON, G. G. "Evolutionary Determinism and the Fossil Record," *Sci. Monthly,* 71 (1950), 262-67.

———"The World into which Darwin Led Us," *Science,* 131 (1960), 966-74.

Cause and Effect in Sociology

TALCOTT PARSONS

SINCE the chairman has called attention to the long duration of my career, I may report my impression that intellectual climates in the field of social science have changed appreciably since I was a graduate student in the twenties and beginning to be self-conscious about issues of the sort we are discussing. At that time things were very different indeed, and I would like to make a few of the changes which have occurred the main theme of what I have to say. Perhaps I won't be as specifically sociological as some of you might wish; I am more concerned with the more general problems in social science.

I suppose the chairman's reference to "cause and effect" as being a "granddaddy" can have a number of meanings. I should interpret it to refer to the methodology of science more in the European than in the American sense. We tend, at least in my branches of it, to think of methodology as meaning research techniques, but the present concern is rather the type of methodology that borders on the philosophy and logic of science. Here, the problems are so interconnected that almost wherever you begin you must raise practically all of the crucially important ones before you throw light on the one with which you began.

THE CONCEPT OF A SYSTEM OF INTERDEPENDENT VARIABLES

In the middle to late nineteen-twenties and early thirties, discussions of the relations between social and the physical and biological sciences made much of the distinction between "cause and effect" reasoning and reasoning about mutual interdependence in systems. Most important to me is the influence of L. J. Henderson, especially his discussions of the work of Pareto and his insistence that Pareto was far in advance of his fellow social scientists. Hen-

51

derson was fond of emphasizing that Pareto became a social scientist only late in life after a thorough training in mathematical physics—as it stood in his time, of course. Thoroughly schooled in the conception of systems of interdependence, he carried this model over from physics into mathematical economics and from there, in a much less precise sense, into sociology, in his last major work.

The Henderson-Pareto episode and all the intellectual issues that revolved about it approximately twenty-five years ago, here in Cambridge, belong to the past, but to an important chapter in American intellectual history. Since I was a young man very much involved in these things, it made an indelible impression on me.

I would therefore like to take as a point of departure something like the Henderson-Pareto conception of a system of interdependence. But I may suggest four respects in which this formula was too general to characterize the kind of conceptualization that social science as a whole and sociology in particular have to employ. Some problems implied by these considerations can then be spelled out.

LEVELS OF ORGANIZATION

The first problem not taken account of in the model of mutual interdependence that I brought up was that of levels of hierarchy of organization. The interdependence idea was that one defined a certain set of variables which in some sense were logically equivalent to each other on a single level. Then one investigated their interdependences in systems.

I was by that time aware of a somewhat different way of looking at the functioning of organisms. A very important model was the work of W. B. Cannon, which he put in form accessible to the layman in his popular book *The Wisdom of the Body*—the concept of homeostasis, of the maintenance of equilibrium through regulatory mechanisms. This was equilibrium theory of a different sort from the Paretian adaptation of physical equilibrium for his economics; it emphasized organization and control.

The development of information theory and of cybernetic ideas which started from engineering and certain branches of the physical sciences, although it feeds into a somewhat similar conception of certain classes of systems, does not necessarily affect all systems of interdependence. The important idea here is that low-energy systems that process information can exercise certain kinds of control over the behavior of high-energy systems. The idea has recently become accepted that this type of system is particularly important in the life sciences and in the social sciences—the sciences of behavior, in particular. Gradually, many biologists and some behavioral scientists have come to think of this as very much related to the concept of adaptation in the more general biological sense. It suggests that adaptation involves actively selective control over environments rather than stressing its adjustive aspects. This is one major context of variation. Henderson, as a philosopher of science, did not emphasize sufficiently this aspect of living systems.

THE GENETIC REFERENCE

The second big context has been discussed over the years in all these disciplines. It is the problem of the existence and significance of irreversible temporal processes, and includes the growth of the individual organism. While there is a sense in which development, or growth, is considered one alternative to disorganization and dissolution, it would seem that the structure of these alternatives is far from symmetrical. The problem of irreversibility relates to that of cycles in some aspects of history, including the business cycle. It is, of course, also relevant to the broadest sweep of biological thinking in that the concept of evolution is very much involved. Such irreversible change does not result from the simple balancing out of forces in equilibrium or interdependence. One must introduce some further conceptual elements to account for it. And yet these are properties that have to be taken into account in the study of living systems, whether at the subhuman biological level or at the human, social, cultural, psychological levels. The continuities among these levels are coming increasingly to the fore.

Now, on top of these two modifications of simple equilibrium theory, appear two others. One is not a central preoccupation of sociologists, though it has become a focus of more attention by the other sciences, and the other raises big questions from any point of view, but is undoubtedly central in the social and cultural fields and particularly in sociology. The first of these two problems is what you might call the cultural reference.

THE CULTURAL REFERENCE

What I have in mind is the involvement in behavior of processes and mechanisms and their resultants, which we think of under such categories as meaning, symbolization, and the like. Language is one of the central prototypes of this kind of phenomena. For a long time the anthropological and linguistic point of view was that human language was almost a sport, unrelated to any other phenomenon known to science. A most interesting article by Professor Hockett of the University of Michigan appeared in the September, 1960, *Scientific American*, an issue devoted to social evolution in the context of the evolution of life. While linguistic scientists have avoided long discussions of the problem of evolution, partly because of the paucity of tangible evidence of transitional stages, Hockett says that it simply doesn't make sense to think of language as just being there without having evolved, and that the problem of the transitional stages has to be faced. He makes certain interesting suggestions as to the kinds of things that may have happened on the way from sign behavior to the full development of language. This is obviously a very technical question. It feeds into the whole set of problems concerning "ideal" and "material" factors in the determination of human behavior. Indeed, the scientific respectability of the science of linguistics goes a considerable way to undermine the naïve positivism that says, "This sort of thing can't possibly be important." There are many other kinds and classes of evidence, but the great traditions of sociology have developed a heavier prior investment than have certain other social disciplines (e.g., experimental psychology) in the presumptive importance of symbolic systems in relation to behavior. Bridges to the other disciplines in the life sciences have not previously been available, but we have recently been seeing some of the bridges beginning to take shape, notably in the microbiology of the genes. This definitely relates to my first set of qualifications of simple equilibrium theory having to do with levels of organization and control.

Let me give a particularly important example. There is one social discipline lurking on the boundary of social science, with which the sociologists and some of the others, such as the historians, have not come to terms: namely, the law. Law involves a highly codified system of the normative rules that operate in the regulation of human behavior in complex societies. A very sophisticated body of knowledge exists not only about the content of these rules but also about the processes by which they are evolved, defined, applied, and implemented. There has not, however, been much serious analysis outside the legal fraternity itself. One of the reasons for the lack is the "behavioristic" or old-fashioned "hard-science" presumption against the importance of norms since they are "only" symbolic. But I submit that a strict, old-style behavioristic theory of law would not be promising. One must have a conceptual scheme that makes allowance for these normative and symbolic factors and mechanisms before one can build a scientific analysis of human behavior.

THE AUTONOMY OF SUBSYSTEMS

The last of the four main points I wanted to raise is very important. In talking about the kinds of systems we are dealing with, that is, systems that involve multiple levels of organization and hierarchical sets of control mechanisms, we must be careful not to think of "control" in terms too close to human common sense. We do not need to postulate a fellow who sits up somewhere giving orders. For instance, the code components of a language, which controls communication in terms of that language, illustrates one major type of control. For many of the most important processes there need not be any particular human agent who is making decisions about how a system shall operate. In this respect linguistics is of a piece with economics in its analysis of the marketplace and the mechanisms whereby—through supply and demand, price determination, allocation of resources, and determination of volume —the production of different commodities comes about with conscious decision-making only one aspect of the process. However unpopular (and of course inadequate) the older laissez-faire theories have become, there is a basic conception of systems operating at least partially without central planning that is not altogether obsolete in the economic field.

A crucial focus of this problem is the place and the kind of autonomy enjoyed or not enjoyed by subsystems within complex systems. There is a broad sociological point of view that has had to gain acceptance the hard way because of certain features of our cultural traditions. It is that human individuality is in some sense differentiated out of, and hence relative to, cultural and social systems. These systems have aspects that are not understandable in terms of the old-style way of looking at the individual, but they have to be looked at in terms of the macroscopic interactive processes involving many individuals.

The perspective I refer to has developed in different connections. A purely individualistic theory of the functioning of language simply will not work. If one ignores the presence of other speech communicants and of the common factors—codes, speech norms, and so on—that operate, one cannot understand the functioning of language as a system. The same is true of legal norms, and of those things we call social structure. It has become an increasingly broad conviction that this is true of very deep layers and elements of the personality of the individual. There was a most remarkable convergence in this respect. One major source has been the study of the individual as such in which I think the greatest name is still Sigmund Freud. The later work of Freud converged with results of the study of suicide from a sociological point of view; here the most prominent name is still Emile Durkheim. Both came to the conclusion, basically, that certain crucial goals and norms of the individual had to be understood as derived from his society and culture. In other words, society and culture were not only an environment for individuals but were in part constitutive of the structure of their personalities.

It is through lines of reasoning of this sort that such a concept as institutionalized individualism—to use a bit of sociological jargon—has become crystallized. By this I refer to the idea that the degrees of freedom that make autonomous behavior possible are dependent on an individual's integration in a superindividual matrix. For instance, if one does not know their language one is not really free to comunicate with his fellows, and yet language is not an individual phenomenon. I cite a classic example from Durkheim, namely, his interpretation of the contrast in the rates of suicide between two religious groups, Catholics and Protestants, with Protestants characterized by substantially higher rates. The issue that Durkheim discussed is: What is the nature of the sense in which the Protestant is or is not controlled by virtue of his identification as a Protestant? He made the crucial distinction that the Catholic is controlled above all by his membership in the church and the ways in which the authorities of the church prescribe and control his beliefs and practices. In this sense the Protestant is free from the control of the religious organization. The point on which Durkheim focused was that this is freedom from prescription of detailed belief. That is, there is not in the same sense dogma for the Protestant. On the other hand, if he is free from group control, the crucial issue is whether as a Protestant it is open to him either to accept the authority of the church in defining his relation to his God or to exercise his autonomy to take ultimate responsibility himself. The answer is clear. It would contradict the conception of Protestantism if he turned over this responsibility to a church. So if one belongs to the category of Protestant, and if this is a socially effective category, he is not free to relinquish his freedom. This is one case among many others in our society illustrating that freedom is operative within a matrix and not all of this matrix is available to the free individual. That is true of individuals, and it is also true of collectivities. I think that this whole crucial problem of the balance between integrative super-unit factors and smaller units is an issue of great importance in the biological sciences. I know it is an issue of great importance in the social sciences.

In spite of all these so-called qualifications I want to make clear that certain lessons learned in my early years have to stay learned. One example is Whitehead's warning against the fallacy of mis-placed concreteness. This is a matter of being careful to avoid hypostatizing particular conceptual schemes at particular empirical levels. This is to say that it is essential to emphasize a thorough-going relativity of a certain type. When one puts all of these things together, however, this relativity does not at all impugn the idea of the existence of some kind of an evolutionary framework in which what I call the cultural level of organization, and even certain types of subsystem autonomy have their place in a scheme in which a succession of progressively higher levels of organization consti-tute a primary theme.

In other words, I am one of those social scientists who, having gone through a revulsion against the use of evolutionary ideas in his field, has been coming back to them.

Connected with these considerations is the idea, which surely has to be faced by the social sciences of our time, that the development of science itself, both physical and biological, con-stitutes a primary problem for the social scientist, namely, what constellations of human organization and culture have made it possible and probable that modern science should emerge. We know that in several civilizations that have been sophisticated in other respects nothing of the sort happened. Then why has the development of science gathered force in this century on a scale altogether without precedent, and extended from the natural to the behavioral field? This seems to be connected with the self-analysis of human beings at the behavioral and cultural levels—in other words, the emergence of the social and cultural sciences as academic big business. There are still voices in our society which essentially say "You can't do it,' though they are very apt to be characterized by a tell-tale duality or ambivalence; in other words, in one mood the voice says, "It can't be done, it is intrinsically impossible," and in the other it says, "For heaven's sake don't do it because it is dangerous."

STABILITY AND CHANGE

I shall discuss a few of the problems in this area that have been highly controversial in the other fields that are the subject of this colloquium. I would like first barely to mention the problem of structure and process, or, shall we also say, the problem of stability and change. We hear a great deal of discussion of points of view that do not make enough allowance for change or do not make enough allowance for stability. This is mixed up at many points with the cause and effect problem. May I suggest that at the deepest levels of the logic of science it is impossible to study processes without some conception of structure. It is impossible to talk about change without any conception of that which changes. But I find it very convenient to use the related dualities at two levels and to distinguish two fundamental kinds of "dynamic problems" that we have to deal with. We may speak of those which have to do with processes within relatively stable systems, since what at one level of observation is a structure, at another always dissolves into some kind of orderly balance among processes. This is straight relativity; there is no ontological reason to say that either has priority over the other. But if there is no stability at any point for reference, then it is impossible to go on to the analysis of process at the next level.

I would fit such ideas as equilibrium into this conception. Thus, the much discussed concept of function in social science, is, properly defined, indispensable—if not explicitly used it is smuggled in under other names. If one has the conception of a homeostatically controlled boundary-maintaining system that has some stability and therefore to which some such concept as equilibrium is applicable, then all one means by functional analysis is a set of classifications of the problems of such a system—either the conditions under which the stability will be maintained or the conditions under which it will be sufficiently disturbed so that it will go into some other state of organization, or one of disorganization.

There is here a fundamental paradox, namely, that one has a chance of analyzing such a condition if one can speak about a range of variation. This has to do with balances of input and output. A range of variation in that balance means that there are upper and lower limits such that remaining within them is essential to the stability of the system. There are middle ranges that are compatible with stability, and there are border regions where the strain becomes increasingly great. And probably there are threshold phenomena, such that, if the variation goes beyond certain ranges for sufficiently long periods, then irreversible change is the consequence. This is the kind of thing we mean by functional analysis. In my opinion we all use it whether we call it that or not. An aspect of this is the orderly classification of the points in the operation of a system at which these problems can be expected to occur—the specific problem will of course be different at different points.

I would distinguish this sort of functional analysis from that of processes of change in a sequence of structural change. An example would be the processes that are involved in the embryological development of the individual organism, or are involved in the development of the personality, or in the evolutionary or developmental changes of social systems. Now a developmental change of this sort is always a change that involves disturbing and upsetting previous, relatively stable states or equilibria. The system then goes through processes and phases of reorganization and eventually attains some new and different, relatively stable state. This is a basic paradigm with which we all operate.

Among these developmental processes is a process in which the biological and social sciences have in common a focus of interest, namely the differentiation of previously simpler systems into more complex systems and the concomitant development of mechanisms that integrate the newly differentiated parts. I really think the social sciences are just beginning to develop comparative knowledge of these processes of differentiation, and this means the beginning of a comparative morphology of the structures of social systems, and knowledge of how the processes operate, although the latter is still very fragmentary. I do not think this is by any means the whole of the subject matter of social change, but it is central, and we are beginning to have both empirical and theoretical resources to deal with it.

HISTORY AND SOCIOLOGY

This brings me to the much asked question, "Where does history fit in?" There seems to be a kind of moving frontier between these two fields according to which attempts at more generalized theoretical analysis will continually be tried out in dealing with historical problems. In the early phases these attempts will continually run into trouble. They will fail to solve all sorts of problems that many very intelligent and well-informed people know to be of great importance, and they may introduce (and, indeed, often do.) positive misconceptions about these problems. And almost uniformly the reaction in an important part of the intellectual world will be: "You shouldn't have tried to do this analytically; it's a problem for history." From this point of view, history, that is to say the historical perspective, has two crucial foci. First there is the idea of temporal succession, the temporal ordering of phenomena and events. There is, second, the idea of wholeness, which when sufficiently generalized gets to be uniqueness, which says that any attempted analytical breakdown results in positive distortion.

The temporal reference is here to stay. On the other front, however, it is relative to the situation of the time. That is, there always is a historical component, and this is by no means true only of the social field. It is true, of course, of the biological world. And it is most definitely true of the personality of the individual since life history is discussed in very much the same way that collective histories are in the social field. But I would regard it as a moving frontier since, as analytical theory and the organization of empirical evidence around and relevant to that theory develop, many historical problems will cease to be considered as such. But since this is a moving frontier, the historical element does not simply disappear. Its survival is a question of an element of irreducible givens which cannot yet or in a given state of knowledge be analytically treated.

This is a field of controversy in my own discipline right now, as Dr. Coser and Professor Aron can testify. There is a battle going on between the proponents of historical analysis and explanation and the proponents of theoretical-analytical analysis and explanation. Currently this centers on the differences between the so-called "structural-functionalists" and, especially, the neomarvists.

EXPLANATION AND PREDICTION

I would like to deal with another issue and then come to a suggestion that I do not feel terribly confident about, but will introduce. The first brings us specifically to the cause and effect problem: What do we mean by explanation on the one hand, and by prediction on the other? Some people like to say that without prediction and control we have no knowledge. I take a position against that, and suggest that it is precisely this irreducible historical element that gives explanation an advantage over prediction. In other words, the kind of asymmetry that I suggested has been operating in the organization of living systems generally involving the irreversibility factor, applies here at the methodological level.

There is one sense in which explanation of past events is nothing but retrospective prediction. That consists in putting oneself in the position of an observer at the time something happened, predicting what would happen contingent on certain other intervening events, and then saying that the experimental check is: "Did it happen or didn't it happen as predicted?" In these terms the difference between retrospective explanation and prospective prediction is only that in the former case it is possible for the explainer to know what actually did happen, and in the latter case it is not. The real question is: "Does the explainer know more, or is it possible for him to know more?"; and the answer, it seems to me, is very clearly "Yes." It is possible to know what contingent factors in fact came in to influence the result but could not have been predicted. I would relate this difference to the inevitable abstractness of analytical schemes in science along the White-headian lines of the idea of abstractness. The reason why prediction is not as good as the best explanation that takes advantage of historical knowledge, but which is not based solely on historical knowledge, is precisely that there are empirical devices for covering certain of the areas of contingency that an analytical scheme cannot cover in the predictive direction. Furthermore this is more than the element of empirical prediction that consists simply in the extrapolation of empirical temporal trends, which is one device of prediction but not exactly the sort of thing that we are talking about.

I refuse to see here a basic issue of the relative merits of historical and analytical approaches. The view that it is in the onto-logical nature of human culture and society that it must not or cannot be analytically treated seems to me utter nonsense. If we take that view, we are denying the legitimacy or possibility of science in this area.

Lastly, I might just make the suggestion I referred to. Let me return to my starting point and the idea of mutual interdependence without classification of kinds of variables. Of course we must have definitions of variables, but not without qualitative classification of types of variables. Then the question is: "What are the variables?"; and, therefore, how do we trace the kinds of consequences that we can call effects of their operation? I suggest merely that we would make a great deal of progress if we would attempt to keep in mind that these causes and effects are not all of the same sort. If the picture I have been trying to sketch of the kinds of systems we are operating with is anywhere near the workable picture of our stage of development in these fields, we have got to make some important qualitative distinctions among types of causes, that is, types of causal factors.

Let me just suggest two of the bases of such a classification.

One is the whole idea of levels of organization. This implies that it makes a crucial difference at what point in a given series of logical heredity—of such ideas as race, or of values or ideals, and used to be violent controversies over whether one had geographical explanations of social phenomena or explanations in terms of biological heredity, of such ideas as race, or of values or ideas, and so on. I think these arguments are essentially over, partly because we have learned to discriminate these levels and to recognize that these are not either/or questions, but questions of how different things fit into the hierarchy of levels of organization. Particularly if we accept the general idea of a basic hierarchy of levels of organization, we are often dealing with intermediate systems, in the sense that there is reason to postulate levels of organization in their environment below them and levels above them. It is crucially important to distinguish from what type of source an environmental influence comes.

A very simple psycho-sociological example would be the personality development of the child. Unquestionably, malnutrition can influence that development. And certain types of social attitudes of the parents which are not biochemically analyzed can also influence that development. These are influences that operate at different levels of organization, and it does not make sense to treat them as flatly comparable with each other. The socialization influence operating through parental attitude is the source of the internalized culture-and-object organization of the personality. This is just as much an empirical process as the biochemistry of the digestive process. But it is a different type of empirical process. The same kind of discriminations can be made with reference to internal types of factors or causes. I happen to think that the best device we have for making such discriminations is functional classification. With respect to functional classifications, I think the social and biological sciences are essentially on comparable ground. Such classification is a way of making qualitative discriminations about the significance of causal factors and thus formulating the questions we ask about their effects on a system in such a way as to get away from the more simple-minded version of the mere interdependence of variables.

DISCUSSION
Cause and Effect in Sociology

QUESTION: A set of rules to generate the sentences of English and nothing else is relative. With it one has a way to approach speech acquisition and hopes to find some kind of invariant order because one gets at fundamentals rather than such physical aspects of speech as vocabulary. What are the most promising lines of arriving at a finite description of these fundamentals?

PARSONS: My own knowledge of linguistics is extremely spotty, but I have the impression that after going through various stages—the traditional concern with grammar and syntax and vocabulary, and then the enormous development of phonetics—we have a sufficiently developed set of basic classifications of components and ways in which they can be combined and of levels of organization of language systems so that not only comparative structural morphology but comparative ranges of variation, which have relatively few yawning gaps in them, can be constructed. Hence we have an opportunity to raise more general problems, because we can actually trace variability in determinate terms. I think the social and cultural sciences are making appreciable progress in the development of empirical knowledge of social organizations at many different levels, indicating ways of categorizing and classifying data about them that facilitate comparability.

QUESTION: In some ways I think the sociologists' descriptions are a little like those of linguistics. The sociologists can talk about certain institutions, but cannot arrive at a compact description of the whole system. We cannot do that in linguistics either. I think there is some promise in the idea that norms in general might be treated as rules-systems, as you would treat grammatical norms. There are certain parallels, for instance, the way in which a child irons out his language to a simpler system than it is. It is a little like the way in which, perhaps more at adolescence than at earlier ages, people inducted into a set of norms tend to treat them as uncontingent on sets of rules. This implies a simpler structure than actually exists.

PARSONS: I am sure there are analogies of that sort. It is the kind of thing I had in mind in the very elliptical references I made to the subject of law. At one level I think the historical-legal systems are by far the richest mine of codified knowledge of systems in the human-social field. The lawyers' and the sociologists' interests in them have only here and there begun to make real contact with each other. I am inclined to think that the best contact has been made in certain historical fields in the work of what one might call institutional historians—that is, legal and economic and social historians—even though they have different perspectives. They have had to be deeply concerned with these things. If the kind of knowledge of restricted cases that the best historians have been able to work out can be built into broader classificatory schemes, advance this sort of thing could be very rapid.

QUESTION: I would certainly agree that enormous strides have been made in kinship as in language studies. But, I would like to come back to another point that Professor Parsons raised, as a person who is deeply interested in this problem of process. I would like to have him develop it a little bit. That is the idea that you have processes at a higher level of organization which become a kind of stable system for analysis of another set of processes in another stable system. Can we really explain this?

PARSONS: There are many examples in the literature of institutional history in this broad sense I am talking about. I think these examples are beginning to get codified into something a little different from the older talk about "progress" without differentiating the stages of "process." Look at Walt Rostow. Even such a scheme as traditional transitional take-off and maturing processes of economic growth is an attempt in this direction at codification.

Incidentally there is, as you are aware, a very important connection (which might have to do with the discussions that have gone on at M.I.T.) between the Rostow idea of traditional society and the Lerner idea of traditional society—though Lerner was not looking at economic growth but at the development of communication systems. Professor Hagen's work is also involved with many problems of this sort.

The idea is: a traditional society doesn't just automatically, and without explanation, shift over in the kind of direction you are talking about. It is reasonable, within certain limits and with adequate evidence, to postulate a certain stability of these features —and therefore to regard any process by which that stability can be sufficiently shaken up to initiate major change as a problem. Then we need to look for specific kinds of influences that can bear on that at specific points.

QUESTION: I would like to make two remarks. The first would be just on the side issue; the other will be more fundamental. The first is that I would take exception to the contradiction you show between saying it cannot be done and we cannot face the consequences. The two propositions simply cannot be put into agreement: (a) it is not a science and (b) it pretends to be a science and the consequences of this false science are very detrimental [laughter].

The second remark is that you had great difficulty in your lecture using the terms "cause and effect." I must say, when I came to the colloquium, my great curiosity was: "How can Professor Parsons deal with a concept he normally does not use?" The main impression I got was a repetition of my own difficulty—the evident inference that this concept does not belong in my vocabulary. Quite clearly, the concept of cause and effect does not really belong in your vocabulary. From time to time you wanted to remind the audience that you were dealing with cause and effect, because here and there you employed these words. But clearly you were bored with this wordage, because it had no place in your conceptual framework.

What you want to do is analyze system, process, function— and for this, quite clearly, the word cause is unnecessary. You run a system based on interrelations between different phenomena. When you try to explain the whole system clearly, you cannot find one phenomenon or one factor. So, from time to time, you say "influence." Then you remember the title of this colloquium. If I am wrong you will correct me, but my impression is that you could do without the concept "cause and effect."

PARSONS: Oh, I think so. I might use in extenuation the metaphor introduced by the chairman, namely that grandchildren think somewhat differently from their parents. He referred to this question of causality as the granddaddy of them all. But that clearly isn't enough. I think Professor [Raymond] Aron is right. I, and probably most social scientists of my generation, do not habitually use this sort of term. Perhaps the Hendersonian lesson was learned all too well, in a certain sense. The person who, like myself, has paid very special attention to "system" probably shies away more than others. I quite agree with Professor Aron that assertions to the effect that everything is interdependent with everything else are not very helpful. It may be important to assert something along this line as a criticism of naïve, too specific attribution of relations. But it should only be a frame of reference within which to try to pin down more specific relationships.

Now I think probably the term "cause" in our field is most appropriately used in just the sort of situation he outlined—namely, where you have a good logical experimental design, whether it is a contrived experiment or an experiment in nature. At any rate where you have a sufficiently clearly defined similarity in all respects except for some one or two differentiating factors. If you can, pin down a difference of consequence to those factors. This is what every empirical scientist hopes it will be possible to do. It happens, heavens knows, seldom enough in any field, but certainly very seldom in our fields.

I might say this is in the tradition of one of the great forebears of our period, with whose work both Professor Aron and I have occupied ourselves. Max Weber had precisely this conception of the differentiating factor as between two alternative possible courses of events. Some historians will perhaps remember the controversy over the outcome of the Persian wars. Weber claimed there was good evidence that, had there been a Persian victory, the course of development of Western culture would have been very different indeed. The rationalizing influence of Greek culture would have been cut off in favor of a stereotyped religious traditionalism. Now this is a genuine problem in historical causation, whatever you think of the position Weber took in this particular case.

QUESTION: What happens to the process by which a system adjusts to some external force that induces once-over change? It goes back towards an equilibrium. But what happens, if instead, the whole system evolves?

PARSONS: I don't feel any fundamental difficulty in this respect. There is definitely a difference of emphasis. I don't believe we have anything that can be called a really comprehensive classification of types and components of interrelated process. The major people of the previous generation have continually kept coming back to it in one form or another. One way of putting it would be in terms of the Hegelian-Marxian heritage. Even Durkheim, who was perhaps the most equilibrium-minded of the great thinkers of that time, kept raising these problems. The very last phase of his work was concerned with it.

You have a variety of different ideas here. Let me mention only two. If I may bring Alfred Kroeber into this picture, I think Kroeber puts it in a very interesting historical perspective. He shows that there is a bunching of major scientific contributions in particular periods and in locations and also that movements of scientific development get exhausted. In other words, the development of science is not, at the relevant levels, a linear accumulation.

Another type of idea, of a very different sort, is Weber's charismatic breakthrough. You may say that this is, theoretically, a residual category. Even so, it focuses attention on the innovative process.

The other phase I would very much like to stress is that we are getting, in this branch of social science in this country, a very substantial revival of interest in the large-scale society as distinguished from the subsystems of particular organizations and particular communities. Also, we are placing our own large-scale society relative to others both laterally and in historical depth. As this develops, it seems to me the evolutionary perspective mounts in significance. Probably there have been comparable alternations of phase in the history of biological science—a period when practically nobody paid any attention to evolutionary problems, but concentrated on the anatomy and physiology of particular species, and then somehow the comparative problems and the evolutionary focus came back into the center of attention.

QUESTION: Actually I think in both the social sciences and biology the main point is that the word evolution, whatever it stands for, has changed quite a bit. This is particularly true if if you read the anti-evolutionary literature. It does not attack evolution, but only a very specific and particular theory in biology. The term evolution goes back to the eighteenth century, with the French *philosophes,* and ultimately back to Aristotle. It goes back to the idea of free formation, the unfolding of something which was there—ultimately no change, and ultimately something that is almost forced to go a certain way as if it were predestined.

Evolution today is no longer anything predictive, while the earlier evolutionary idea was all predictive. This is the major difference between the earlier evolutionary ideas and the modern ones.

PARSONS: This is a real peril. I think there should be great caution about predicting next steps in nonideological social science, if there is such a thing.

QUESTION: [inaudible]

PARSONS: If I understand correctly, that is very much on the right side. I like to think of there being some sort of variable between the macroorganic considerations that operate in anatomy and physiology and the microanalysis that operates at biochemical levels and, on the other hand, the sociological and psychological levels of analysis of human behavior. I like to think of this from the polemical view of my discipline, vis-a-vis my psychological colleagues. One of the crucial sources of trouble was the systematic ignoring of the fact that learning operated in socially structured situations. The tendency was to isolate the stimulus from any pattern of significance external to the learning organisms. Therefore we might have learned quite a lot about certain processes of learning, but we didn't learn how essentially important things got learned. The learning of language gets into a very different level from this point of view.

Now, I think that these connections have begun to be established over a fairly wide front. From the psychological side it was Freud who pushed the deepest. So that psychology has acquired a new dimension of significance—i.e., organization relative to the personality—and the other side of it is the fact that the social sciences have acquired a new dimension of depth. So we now have the possibility, as you suggest, of really getting to understand mechanisms. Previously we had almost to bypass the whole mechanism problem and say "Well, we can lay out morphologically certain patterns of what did happen but we can't understand how."

Let me just mention one very interesting example. Many of our people who are interested in the small-group phenomenon have turned up patterns of growth behavior that are surprisingly like, in certain features, Freud's famous myth of the primal patricidal crime. This appears mainly where there is a leadership structure in a group—a ganging up of all of the people, in some symbolic sense, to get rid of the leader. Well now, you can say this is not literally killing the father, but there seems to be a very deep seated pattern here. Even if it isn't literally what Freud postulated, his idea is simply not to be brushed aside.

QUESTION: Let me raise another methodological question. I think Professor Aron's sense of cause in the second definition implies a system that is not only in equilibrium but has facility of equilibrium. This applies in the specific sense used in mathematics and physical sciences rather than talking about functionalism in the more general sense. When a is 8, b is 5; and when a is 10, b will be 7; and when a is 12 b will be 9. But if a happens to move by some random effect 6-8, and b changes from 5 to 7, this in turn causes a change in c which pulls a back to where it was. The set together tends to hold the thing in equilibrium. That being so, you have a cause which will cause some change in the system if something happens from the outside to change the relationship of *a* and *b* so that when *a* is 7 this causes *b* to be something else than it was originally.

Now if I am right, then you can talk about a cause as something that interferes, something that changes the original set of functional relationships. In a sense this can happen only from the outside and this change will occur whenever some force impinges from the outside. Here and there in your writing, you refer briefly to boundary maintenance. You say in effect—if I misquote you, you tell me—a system that is worth studying has boundary maintenance. If I understand this, it seems to imply that a system will repel this effect from the outside, something outside won't change it. I have never been able to understand the logic of your concept of boundary maintenance and I wonder if, in this context, you could say something about it.

PARSONS: Well, I think I can say something about it. The crucial point is to distinguish two kinds of effect, without any presumption as to which will operate. This will depend on the empirical situation. But I would start, I think, with the theory that you are not dealing with the kinds of system that most of us talk about unless two conditions are presumptively given. That is, unless there is independent variability of events internal to the system and events external to it—as in Cannon's well-known example of variance of body temperature. Internal body temperature is maintained nearly constant under normal conditions, external temperature may vary in a considerable range and *is* continually varying in the typical case.

The other condition is again relevant to this model, namely, that in the respects in which we are interested the internal state of the system is stabler than the relevant features of the external system. When I say "stabler," I allow for orderly change—a "growth pattern" or something like that. This is a form of stability. Now, in this situation a variation coming to the system from an exogenous source may be neutralized if it has a potentially disturbing effect on the internal state. In other words it may activate counteracting processes. So, the system remains closer to its initial state than it would have been had these counteractions not operated, given the external disturbance. This would be a boundary-maintaining or equilibrating process. The other type of effect upsets the balance. Then the system as a whole has to come to some new adjustment, like your example of the *a* and *b,* and then *c.* So that the generalization about uniformity or stability, on the first set of assumptions, would have to be changed.

The point I would like to make is that unless you make this kind of a distinction, you cannot really have an orderly analysis of change itself. It is a theoretical point of view which also has to be an empirical generalization. Social systems do in fact typically have this order of stability, so that not every effect is proportionate to its cause. I think this is essentially what I am trying to say.

QUESTION: Why do you call this boundary maintenance rather than some particular equilibrium value?

PARSONS: I don't know that you need to. Let me put one consideration here that may seem rather strange. There is a sense in which, perhaps to the biologist, the boundaries of most systems are very tangibly there. That is, skins, cell membranes, organ membranes, and so on. One of the great difficulties in social science is delineating just these boundaries. Common sense doesn't tell us what the lines are. One inference from that might be that there *aren't* any significant lines. Where common sense does tell us about the lines—national boundaries, for example—the result is clear. But in the many cases that are not clear on a common sense basis, it seems very important to try to be precise about it. That is the main basis on which I justify it.

Cause and Effect in the Study of Politics

ROBERT A. DAHL

The notion of natural law is indefinite enough for it to be a thankless task to try precisely to distinguish natural laws within the class of true constant conjunctions. The case is even worse if one attempts to pick out from within the class of natural laws those that should, in some special sense, be called "causal laws." I shall not attempt this thankless task. . . . R. B. Braithwaite, *Scientific Explanation.*

The word "cause" is so inextricably bound up with misleading associations as to make its complete exclusion from the philosophical vocabulary desirable. . . . Bertrand Russell, "On the Notion of Cause."

EXPLICATION of the notion of cause had, I think, better be left to the philosophers, and I gladly yield the privilege to Professor Nagel. I propose to assume a different task, namely, to examine the ways in which different notions of cause have influenced the development of empirical explanations of political phenomena. By explanation, I mean simply the subsuming of a particular event or class of events, the occurrence of which we wish to "explain," under a more general law or hypothesis that we believe to be true. An explanation is empirical to the extent that it can be confirmed or proven false by experience.

The systematic study of politics is shot through with varying notions of cause. Indeed, this was the case from the beginning. It is hardly surprising that an intellectual discipline owing so much to Aristotle should have been influenced by his notions of material, efficient, formal, and final cause.

I propose therefore to examine the role, in empirical political studies, of four kinds of explanation that are associated with notions of cause. These are purposive, teleological, functional, and what I would like to call "strictly causal" explanations.

I. PURPOSIVE EXPLANATIONS

If a friend tells me that he voted for *K* (or *N*) in the last election, and if I ask him why, he might feel that my question is impertinent, but he probably would not feel that it was foolish. He might well answer that he voted for *K* (or *N*) in order to obtain a certain goal—peace, economic stability, or a job in the local post office. Such an answer obviously implies a belief in a regularity of the general form: If *A* happens, then *B* will (or probably will) occur. It also implies a purpose or goal: I do *A* in order to achieve *B*; that is, my purpose is *B*.

I mention purposive explanations because some people argue that explanations involving purpose must necessarily be different in a fundamental way from the kinds of explanations provided by empirical science. Hence, it is said, the study of politics cannot be an empirical science. Although I do not think this argument is valid, it has had a profound effect on the study of politics—perhaps most of all on the mood and approach of the student himself. The argument usually takes one of two forms.

The first follows from the fact that the goal to be achieved by a purposive action lies in the future. Hence, it is said, a future event causes a present event. This notion is violently at odds with most conceptions of causation used in the empirical sciences. Since it has been disposed of by many different critics,[1] I shall not dwell on it. The fact is, of course, that my friend votes for *K* (or *N*) *now* in order to bring about a *future* state of affairs. To the extent that he is influenced by that future state of affairs, he is influenced by expectations, goals, and evaluations that are present in his mind *before* or at the time he makes his final decision, not *after* he has already cast his vote.

The second argument is usually stimulated by words like "values" or "evaluations," which you will note I have just used in describing the elements of my friend's decision to vote for *K*

---

[1] For example, by Braithwaite, *Scientific Explanation* (Cambridge: Cambridge University Press, 1955), 324-25.

or *N*. It is said that since the achievement of purpose necessarily requires evaluations of alternatives, and since evaluations are a reflection of one's values or ethical standards, therefore the study of politics necessarily involves ethics.

Many critics reject this argument. They say it is persuasive only if it rests on a confusion between empirical and normative propositions and that careful analysis of these two sorts of propositions would eliminate the confusion. I agree, but I do not think it would be profitable to go into what has become a rather unproductive controversy. Although I am satisfied myself that a careful analysis reveals the argument to be spurious, the debate still goes on, as a reading of almost any issue of a political science journal will show.[2]

Instead of pursuing this criticism I should like to suggest that these controversies might also result from conflicting conceptions of what constitutes an explanation. Thus one might say: "When I ask you why you vote the way you do, I don't want an explanation simply in causal terms. To me, a satisfying explanation would require you to justify your action, that is, to explain it as a logically necessary consequence of, or at least as logically consistent with, some standards of conduct to which you hold, and to which . . . perhaps . . . I hold also."

In reply . . . a student of politics interested in empirical explanation might say: "But I wish to distinguish between empirical explanations and normative evaluations. In some of my roles— as teacher, perhaps, or father, or citizen, or publicist, or even as political philosopher—I may wish to make evaluations. When I do make evaluations it is perfectly proper for you to ask me why, and I should be obliged to try to justify my action to you in the way you have suggested. But in my other role, as social scientist, when I try to explain something, I do not try to justify it. I simply try to account for it by deriving it from some more general proposition that describes a regular sequence which we believe does

---

[2] See, for example, C. A. McClelland, "The Function of Theory in International Relations," *The Journal of Conflict Resolution* (September, 1960), 303-36.

hold in the world of politics. Thus, if you ask me why a revolution occurred in Cuba, I might propose to explain it by referring to the hypothesis of Aristotle: "Revolutions . . . occur when the sections of the state which are usually regarded as antagonists —for example, the rich and the common people—are equally balanced, with little or nothing of a middle class to turn the scale." (*Politics,* 1304 a, b) Aristotle's hypothesis may be false of course, or the case of Cuba may not fit, but my explanation surely does not require me to evaluate the Cuban revolution!

Lest I seem to claim too much, or to suggest a defensiveness about the study of politics that I do not intend, let me make clear the limits of what I am saying. It is altogether possible that certain aspects of human purpose in politics will indeed make the study of politics lag behind other empirical disciplines in the rigor of the analysis employed and the degree to which theories are confirmed. However, I do not think this will happen because the study of politics is saddled with a purposive explanation that must necessarily contain nonempirical elements absent from other empirical studies. Rather, the lag will occur, I think, because of certain characteristics of human purposes in politics.

Men's purposes in politics are extraordinarily various, any single purpose can usually result in a great variety of political acts and, conversely, any political act can result from a great variety of purposes. Men's purposes change, and the instruments they employ also change. Men's purposes are obscure and complex; they are intervening variables; they are inferred or hypothetical entities not directly observable; yet they are evidently indispensable to political analysis.

In political analysis, attempts to cope with the variety, obscurity, and complexity of purposes by hypothesizing some single intervening instrumental activity—such as gaining power, office, or votes—has helped to produce some interesting and useful theories, like those of Hobbes or, more recently, Downs. So far, however, the predictive power of such theories as compared with that of common sense has not been very great.

II. TELEOLOGICAL EXPLANATIONS

Purposive explanations of political phenomena are close both in spirit and in meaning to teleological explanations. Teleological explanations, however, seem to offer something more. The purposes in question are cosmic rather than strictly human.

It is possible to distinguish several different kinds of emphasis in what are often called teleological explanations. One emphasis, which I have already mentioned in connection with purposive explanations, concerns a final state that succeeds in time the events it is said to cause. This is the essence or nature of the thing. The notion of the time sequence involved here is from a strictly causal viewpoint paradoxical. A second emphasis in teleological explanations is on the notion that the purpose of a system cannot always be explained as a resultant of the purposes of the individual elements. The purpose of the whole system is more than the aggregate of the purposes of individual parts. The system is thought to have a purpose of its own apart from those of individuals within it. Closely related to both of these is an emphasis on the idea that we can somehow infer the purposes and actions of the individuals in a system from a knowledge of the purposes of the whole system. If the system has its own purposes, then the individuals must in some sense participate in that purpose.

Teleological explanations are, of course, ancient in the study of politics. Aristotle opens Book I of the *Politics*[3] as follows:

Observation shows us first, that every polis (or state) is a species of association, and, secondly, that all associations are instituted for the purpose of attaining some good—for all men do all their acts with a view to achieving something which is, in their view, a good. We may therefore hold that all associations aim at some good, and we may also hold that the particular association which is the most sovereign of all, and includes all the rest, will pursue this aim most, and will thus be directed to the most sovereign of all goods. This most sovereign and

[3] *The Politics of Aristotle*, trans. by Ernest Barker (Oxford: The Clarendon Press, 1948), 1-6.

inclusive association is the polis, as it is called, or the political association. (1252a)

Because it is the completion of associations existing by nature, every polis exists by nature, having itself the same quality as the earlier associations from which it grew. It is the end or consummation to which those associations move, and the nature of things consists in their end or consummation; for what each thing is when its growth is completed we call the nature of that thing. (1252b) . . . Again the end, or final cause, is the best. Now self-sufficiency is the end, and so the best.

From these considerations it is evident that the polis belongs to the class of things that exist by nature, and that man is by nature an animal intended to live in a polis.

The polis is prior in the order of nature to the family and the individual. The reason for this is that the whole is necessarily prior to the part. (1253a)

An empirical mind of the present day is likely to be mystified and even repelled by this mode of reasoning. A modern critic might respond as follows: The ideas of causality contained in these statements of Aristotle either can be reduced to strictly causal notions of the kind one encounters in empirical analysis, or they cannot. If they can, well and good; we shall treat much of his language as mere metaphor; in this way, perhaps, we can rescue some of the ideas themselves if they happen to be worth rescuing. If, however, the ideas of causality in these statements cannot be reduced to strictly causal notions of an empirical sort, then what meaning can they possibly have? On what grounds are we to decide whether to accept or to reject teleological explanations that are not merely metaphorical equivalents of strictly causal explanations?

The critic would be, in my view, wholly in the right. When we strip the statement of metaphor, all the empirical significance that can be assigned to "Man is by nature an animal intended to live in a polis" can be exhausted by statements employing ideas of causal explanation exactly like those in modern empirical science.

One might ask, nonetheless, what impact teleological explanations have had on the study of politics since Aristotle's day. The impact has not been wholly disadvantageous. Teleological explanations have helped to maintain a sense of the need to account for the development, growth, or evolution of political systems. A political system is seen as the product of a lengthy process of growth, and this growth must somehow be accounted for.

Yet even in this respect the record is spotty. In the first place, Aristotle's teleological explanations may have been made at the expense of more naturalistic accounts of the evolution of man and political systems. These accounts, if we are to accept Havelock,[4] were present in Greek life until they were distorted and inundated by the works of Plato and Aristotle. They were then almost totally lost to the traditions of political science. Even in modern times it has not been political scientists who have studied the political systems of preliterate peoples, but anthropologists. Today, when we are confronted by the need for a well-grounded theory of political development, only a handful of political scientists is in a position to contribute much.

Secondly, emphasis on the final, or "natural," condition of man in political society led, until a generation or so ago, to an almost total neglect of the political aspects of associations other than the state.

Thirdly, this emphasis often led to a conclusion which should have been considered only as a hypothesis, namely, the primacy of politics in the life of man. This assumption has dominated political analysis over the past two thousand years, and it remains today an axiom in a good deal of thinking about politics. Yet the slightest concern for the evidence furnished by experience reveals that for the great bulk of mankind politics is relatively remote from the central core of personality. Indeed, if we must have an axiom, it would probably be healthier to assume that man is not by nature a political animal. We should then find it necessary to explain why a few persons are exceptions to this rule.

[4] Eric A. Havelock, *The Liberal Temper in Greek Politics* (New Haven: Yale University Press, 1957).

It might be said that teleological explanations of political phenomena were never intended to have empirical import. They were intended to have only normative significance. That is, one introduces the notion of the purposes of political associations not in order to make predictions but in order to arrive at evaluations and standards of performance. It would take us far afield to examine this argument; yet even if the point were conceded, teleological explanations have probably been more of a handicap than an advantage because they have tended to build into the study of politics the confusion between normative and empirical that I mentioned earlier. The persuasiveness of teleological explanations in deriving standards of conduct lies precisely in the fact that one seems to be talking about empirical experience—somehow, one appears to deduce moral norms from factual propositions.

Doubtless I have already spent far too much time on a kind of explanation that appears to be only a straw man. My justification is that teleological explanations have been so much a part of political analysis for the past two thousand years that the great, sprawling corpus of political thought is interlaced with them.

III. FUNCTIONAL EXPLANATIONS

Purposive and teleological explanations are both similar to functional explanations; in fact all three are sometimes treated as equivalent. By a functional explanation, however, I mean one which, in describing the behavior of a system, refers to the contributions made by parts of the system to the operation of the whole system.

Functional explanation is widespread in political analysis. Consider, for example, Carl J. Friedrich's well known work, *Constitutional Government and Democracy*.[5] Under the heading, "functional and behavior aspects" of bureaucracy, Friedrich says: "Turning first to the relations of the members of an organization, we find that they are elaborated and defined with reference to the functions to be performed. We may therefore call this group of elementary

[5] (revised ed., Boston: Ginn & Co, 1950).

aspects functional criteria. These simple functional criteria . . . still are far from being fully carried out. Practically all modern governments have struggled time and again to revamp their administrative pattern in terms of these basic functional relationships, but . . . there are always many vested interests ready to resist such simplification and reform." Friedrich then discusses three functional criteria of bureaucracy, namely, centralization of control and supervision, differentiation of functions, and qualification for office.[6]

Other writers who do not use the word "function" have a notion roughly similar to that of function. Thus, Ranney and Kendall discuss the "role" of the American party system and list as achievements or tasks performed by American parties such things as organizing elections, organizing the government, democratizing the constitutional system, and nurturing consensus.[7]

Lasswell has written extensively of seven political functions, intelligence, recommendation, prescription, invocation, application, appraisal, and termination.[8]

More recently, in a bold and imaginative attempt to develop a theory of politics adapted to developing areas, Almond has set out what he calls "a functional approach to comparative politics." He suggests that ". . . the same functions are performed in all political systems, even though these functions may be performed with different frequencies, and by different kinds of structures." However, "The functional categories which one employs have to be adapted to the particular aspect of the political system with which one is concerned. . . . The particular functional categories which we employ in this book were developed for the purpose of comparing political systems as whole systems; and particularly for comparing modern Western ones with the transitional and traditional." Almond then goes on to propose seven functional

[6] *Ibid.*, p. 45ff.

[7] Austin Ranney and Willmoore Kendall, *Democracy and the American Party System* (New York: Harcourt, Brace & World, 1956), pp. 488ff.

[8] Harold D. Lasswell, "The Decision Process: Seven Categories of Functional Analysis," in Polsby, Dentler and Smith, eds., *Politics and Social Life* (Boston: Houghton Mifflin, 1963), 93-105.

categories, as follows: "Input functions—political socialization and recruitment, interest articulation, interest aggregation, and political communication. Output functions—rule-making, rule-application, rule-adjudication." [9]

What precisely is a "function?" In political analysis, as, I take it, in biology, the term is not without ambiguity. An element in a system performs a function to the extent that it contributes to the operation of the whole system. Admittedly this is both vague and excessively abstract.

Perhaps the notion can be clarified by asking in what respects, if any, a functional explanation is different from a strictly causal explanation. Whatever the case may be in biology or sociology, in political analysis a functional explanation, insofar at least as it purports to be an empirical explanation, can always be restated either as a strictly causal explanation or as a correlation. Almond states: "What do we mean by the function of political socialization? We mean that all political systems tend to perpetuate their cultures and structures through time, and that they do this mainly by means of the socializing influences of the primary and secondary structures through which the young of the society pass in the process of maturation." [10] At some cost to Almond's meaning, let me, for purposes of exposition, summarize as follows: A function of the primary and secondary structures through which the young of the society pass is to perpetuate the political culture and structure of a society. This is accomplished by producing attitudes appropriate to the political culture and structure.

It is easy to see that the language of function in Almond's theory could be dispensed with. For example, one could say: A, processes occurring in the primary and secondary structures of a society produce B, certain attitudes toward the political system; B perpetuates C, the political culture and structure of a society. That is, A causes B, and B causes C.

But if explanations using the term function can be restated

[9] Gabriel A. Almond and James S. Coleman, *The Politics of the Developing Areas* (Princeton: Princeton University Press, 1960), pp. 11ff.
[10] *Ibid.*, p. 27.

in nonfunctional language, does the functional approach offer any advantages? Does it help the political scientist develop and improve his theories in some way that a concern exclusively for nonfunctional or strictly causal explanations would not? Although the language of function could be translated into the language of strict causality, the functional approach makes important contributions to contemporary political science (note, incidentally, my own use of functional language at this point) because it is a strategy for research or, more broadly, a strategy for the improvement of empirical theory.

First, functional theories are useful when one wishes to emphasize particular standards of performance. The standard in mind may be stability, survival, political equality, freedom, consent, rational choice, military effectiveness, maneuverability, or any other that one feels is relevant. The language of function provides a way of focusing on the particular contributions of different parts of a political system to meeting this standard of performance.

Second, the functional approach may be regarded as a bet on the importance to theory of specifying certain causes, even where their effects cannot be precisely specified. The functional approach may hypothesize that differences in the way in which various functions are performed can be expected to produce significant differences in other aspects of the political system, even though these differences cannot be exactly described or even anticipated. Thus the functional approach focuses attention on the need to search for differences in the effects when a given function is performed, or not performed, or performed in different ways or "amounts."

Third, the functional approach may be regarded as a bet on the importance to theory of specifying certain effects, even where the causes cannot be precisely specified. One might be reasonably sure that X is a common property of political systems even though one cannot state exactly what the antecedents of X are.

Persistence or endurance is a case in point. A political system (suitably defined) endures or persists longer than many of the phenomena that go on inside it. Typically, a political system outlasts a crowd, a committee meeting, a judicial inquiry, an election, a political issue. We observe, in Almond's words, that political systems tend to perpetuate their cultures and structures through time. Functional analysis might be regarded, then, as a bet that by looking at political phenomena with survival or persistence in mind as an outcome one will discover causes somewhere—quite possibly in unexpected places. For example, in trying to explain the stability and persistence of the American political system we may find a causal sequence that includes the playing fields of P.S. 99.

This suggests a fourth contribution of the functional approach, namely directing attention to regularities that lie concealed beneath the surface. This sounds like hardly more than an injunction to probe deeply, which I suppose is a part of the heritage of any serious scholar. Yet I think it is more than that. The distinction between manifest and latent functions has proved useful as a way of focusing the attention of researchers, first, on some important results that need to be accounted for, and, second, on the possibility that the most unlikely institutions and activities may in fact contribute to these results, despite public sound and fury to the contrary.

It may well be that the functional approach is most productive at this time in the study of politics, precisely because regularities in political systems cannot be nicely specified except in propositions with a rather low level of theoretical significance. If one wishes to talk about large-scale events in large-scale political systems, there is bound to be a certain amount of indefiniteness in describing supposed regularities in the system. As is often the case, precision may be bought at the expense of relevance. Since the phenomena of politics are difficult to observe and measure, more precision would not necessarily even make a theory about political systems more testable.

Thus, although the language of function could be dispensed with, contemporary political scientists will no doubt continue to find it a useful language. Insofar as notions of cause and effect are contained in functional theories, these notions can be expressed without great difficulty in strictly causal language. Functional theories are not so much a different form of explanation as a research strategy, a check-list, a way by which informed students of politics place their bets on the variables that it would pay to examine for relationships of causality or other kinds of interaction.

IV. STRICTLY CAUSAL EXPLANATIONS

If we wish to explain an event, *E*, in a strictly causal manner, we consider *E* as an effect and bring it under some generalization of the form: "Every event *C* is accompanied later by an event *E.*" I assume that at least in principle there must be continuity both in time and in space between the event *C* and the event *E*. Then *C* is called the cause, *E* the effect.[11]

Many explanatory hypotheses in political science are, of course, not strictly causal; they simply state correlations or interactions without specifying causality. If, as I have argued, purposive, teleological, and functional theories about politics can be restated in strictly causal language, could the study of politics profitably dispense altogether with the notion of cause and effect? The question is more pertinent than it might first appear, because advances in rigorous sciences like physics and astronomy are said to have reduced reliance on physical laws formulated in strictly causal or time-bound terms.

There are, however, two closely related reasons why the study of politics is not likely to dispense altogether with cause as I have just defined it.

First, the main justification for the study of politics is to facilitate intelligent political choices; we want to understand politics primarily to help us make decisions. Politics is not very satisfactory as a purely contemplative study; surely there are richer and more satisfying alternatives—astronomy, mathematics, literature, and art, for example. Lest I be misunderstood, let me hasten to add that the study of politics often profits from a disregard for immediate social relevance. But sooner or later one returns to the hard fact that political analysis interests us in considerable part

[11] Here I follow Braithwaite, *op. cit.*, pp. 308ff.

because it can be used to guide individual and collective decisions, not merely to understand them.

A policy is an attempt to cope with the future, not simply to account for the past.[12] To be concerned with policy is to focus on the attempt to produce intended effects. Hence policy-thinking is and must be causality-thinking. For example American programs of economic aid have rested upon the simple causal hypothesis that economic distress is likely to cause anti-democratic political responses. Our current interest in redistribution of land in Latin America assumes the causal hypothesis that extreme inequality, with little or no middle class, tends to cause revolution (*pace* Aristotle), that widespread property ownership tends to induce political stability, and so on.

Secondly, several of the key concepts of political science are strictly causal; it seems highly doubtful that we shall soon develop relevant explanatory theory that does not make use of these concepts. I particularly have in mind concepts of power and control, which have played a prominent part in political analysis from the time of the Greeks. One of the oldest and most challenging objectives of political analysis has been to formulate and test the laws governing the distribution of control over political decisions in a political system. It is, I believe, not too much of a distortion of Aristotle to say that he undertook such a task in Book IV of *The Politics*—the first extensive and systematic attempt at empirical analysis of political systems. If among the

[12] The traditional close relationship among politics, law, and ethics has probably stimulated among students of politics a preoccupation not only for policies but also for accounting causally for actions in the past. Both in ethics and in law the notion of responsibility rests on assumptions about strict causation. Not only does the term "cause" have a technical legal meaning as a ground of action or a case in court, but also, the legal process itself is frequently a search for some plausible and strictly causal explanation of certain events, such that a judge or jury can arrive at a judgment as to responsibility for certain consequences. In ethics the idea of moral responsibility involves the paradoxical assumption that an individual should be held responsible for consequences only if he caused these consequences but was himself free not to have caused them. Thus the notion of responsibility implies that in some circumstances an individual's actions are simultaneously a cause and yet themselves uncaused.

definitional properties of a political system one considers the way in which power over decisions is distributed, and the characteristics—social, psychological, ideological, and so on—of the classes of persons to whom varying amounts of power are allocated, then one objective of political science is to formulate laws that will account for the distribution of power in the world of politics.

However, in political discourse, whether by Aristotle, Hobbes, or Lasswell, a relationship of power, influence, control, or authority is a causal relation among two or more human actors (individuals, groups, or other collectivities). One meaning in political discourse of the statement that "*A* has power over *B* with respect to *X*" is simply that *A* (under certain conditions) can cause *B* to act *X* (with a probability of *P*).

To put the matter this way may render the notion of power rather peculiar as a central concept in political science: Does any other field of empirical investigation take cause itself, in this instance cause in interpersonal relations, as an object of study? Perhaps not. One would expect that the progress of political science might be accompanied by a tendency to break down the global concept of power into more specific sets of relationships. This has in fact been happening. Terms like "power," "influence," "authority" dissolve into nothing more than highly abstract categories that are rarely, if ever, used in rigorous discourse. Rigorous discourse instead will rely on statements about more specific relationships. However, the important point is that, even as this change occurs, so long as we in political science are interested in human relationships in which an actor induces a response in other actors, we are also concerned with causal relationships. In short, it is difficult to imagine how students of politics could explain phenomena without notions of this kind.

SUMMARY

Let me now draw these points together. Political analysis is heavily conditioned by a variety of causal notions, ancient and modern. These notions are deeply embedded in the ways of thinking about political matters that educated people throughout the world habitually employ, particularly if they have been much exposed to formal political thought. Indeed, some ways of explaining political phenomena—the purposive and teleological, for example—are natural even to persons with little exposure to formal political thought.

However, these various notions of cause and effect have not always been helpful to empirical political science. Teleological explanations in particular have probably impeded the growth of empirical theory.

Moreover, purposive, teleological, and functional theories of politics furnish no causal hypotheses that cannot be adequately expressed by statements of a strictly causal kind—i.e., by statements about regular sequences with spatial and temporal continuity between the conditions that precede in time, the causes, and the conditions that follow in time, the effects.

In fact, even the important contributions of modern functional theories do not seem to lie in any unique properties of the causal hypotheses described. Rather, the distinctive contribution of functional theory is as a research strategy: it is a bet on the scientific utility of a particular check-list of variables.

Finally, many hypotheses and theories about politics do not and need not embody strictly causal propositions. Nonetheless, because political analysis is rarely divorced entirely from a concern for policies and choices, and probably cannot proceed without close attention to relationships of power, influence, authority, control, and the like, strictly causal propositions have played, now play, and doubtless will continue to play a highly important part in political science.

DISCUSSION

Cause and Effect in the Study of Politics

QUESTION: Assuming that one cannot get an answer to the problem of national power by simply adding up the results of individual community studies, are any political scientists now working on the problem of power at the national level?

DAHL: I do not know any who are working in the same systematic way as those working at the local community level.

QUESTION: I would like to go back to the beginning of your remarks and to the Aristotelian doctrine of the four causes, which have a familiar ring and which have been obscured by the use of the word "cause," because it has come to mean in the West efficient cause; and consequently if we speak of formal cause we are saying something paradoxical in modern Western languages. I think one can escape the paradox by recalling that the original meaning of the idea comes from the use of cause to mean a ground of pleading—which, transposed into the world of explanation of real phenomena with which Aristotle is concerned, means grounds on which one can discuss something. I would like to submit that the modern way of restating the Aristotelian doctrine would be to say there are only four grounds on which anything can be discussed: you can discuss what it is made of, what form it has, what purpose it serves, and what brought it into existence. If one restates the Aristotelian doctrine of cause in this way, then one has a basis for the problem that your paper so admirably dealt with. One can say that any political phenomenon, like any other phenomenon, can be discussed in these four ways. One cannot say that one of these four ways is more relevant than the others because relevance depends upon what one wants to find. I suggest that politics has a most useful function for all of science (and that the physicists are just rediscovering it) because it has never been able to get away from the fact that no discussion of any phenomenon is complete until all four of these ideas have been discussed.

DAHL: I think it is an interesting point and essentially I agree with it. One should, I think, distinguish between grounds of a fruitful discussion and explanations. I think that there is a great gain in clarity if one specifies rather carefully the mode in which he proposes to explain a phenomenon.

QUESTION: Would you care to undertake a criticism of the formal definition of power?

DAHL: If I were to criticize it, I would do so on grounds of utility in a theory of some kind. The formal definition does not distinguish explicitly between interpersonal power and power over natural and mechanical objects, so the first thing I would want to do, simply because it would lead to more interesting results and theory, would be to make this distinction. It seems to me that we in political science are interested in interpersonal power. If one tries to establish a useful definition of personal power, one must elaborate the formal definition of power. For example, the notion of power implies the question: power in respect to what? We cannot simply say that *A* has more power than *B*. It is always enjoined on us to say that *A* has more power than *B* with respect to *C;* that *A* has power over *B* with respect to the action *C*. If one then wanted to elaborate further, one would have to begin by introducing some suitable operational measure, which must vary from one research project to another because data will vary from one kind of project to another. When one introduces an operational measure, one changes in subtle ways the original meaning so that in a sense the operational definition is more important than the abstract one in the actual conduct of research.

QUESTION: I am not quite sure I have captured the relationship, as you see it, between causality and power. This bothers me particularly because it seems to me that the power explanation differs somewhat from the strictly causal explanation rather than being a special case of it. For example, in trying to give a strictly causal explanation of some processes that may occur in bureaucracy I think one might very likely find that the particular phenomenon one is concerned with could be explained logically in terms of habit. And yet, although habit seemed to be sufficient cause in this particular situation, one certainly could not deny that there was a power relationship there. There is always the problem of potential power. Clearly, if there is a power relationship present and somehow a part of the situation, one would have to describe it not in terms of the requirements of a causal explanation but in terms of the requirements of something else. Can you clarify for me how you see these two things as related?

DAHL: Power gets into the discussion for two reasons. First, it is a central notion in the study of politics; and certainly it is essentially, I think—and here is where we may begin to part company—a causal notion. What I mean when I say "essentially" is that if we begin to analyze the context in which we use (or feel that we want to use) the term "power," then what we end up with is a definition or a conception of it that is causal in character. When we say that A is powerful, and we exclude nature and mechanical and physical environment, we mean that A can induce other people to respond to something in some way. This is clearly a causal notion. When one says that the President has more power to influence foreign policy than I have, then I think one means that the President can cause behavior in the State Department or Congress or in Germany or elsewhere that I cannot cause. To use another kind of analogy, in the absence of the action by the person who exercises power, the behavior goes in one direction; when the action by the person who exercises power is introduced, the behavior is in some sense deflected in a different direction.

When you mention habit, here I may have to ask you to clarify the connection in your mind. If you say that Jones in the State Department is doing so and so from habit, do you mean that the habits are built into him, and that to the extent that his action is autonomous there isn't any power relationship? If somebody else can trip off the habitual response, then there is a power relationship. Indeed, one of the efforts of people whom we would ordinarily describe as seeking or manipulating power is precisely to develop habits of behavior in others which they can trip off.

QUESTION: I would like to raise two questions. The first one is directly related to your answer. I see rather easily that power is a central concept in political science, but when you say it is a causal notion or a causal concept I am asking myself if you are not putting together two different things. Either you mean by "cause" just a regular phenomenon or you mean also a sort of productive power, a sort of force producing the effect. I would like very much to know if you are putting the notion of cause and effect in the notion of the force of production.

My second question derives from a comparison between the paper of Professor Parsons and your own paper. Professor Parsons had great difficulty in finding any use for the concept of cause in a system, and you had difficulty in finding use for any other concept than the concept of cause. You seem to admit that any proposition is a causal proposition when it is an empirical proposition. I would like to ask you if you believe that you are able to reconstruct the system of politics just with certain rigid causal propositions?

DAHL: The only meaning that is strictly causal in the notion of power is one of regular sequence: that is. a regular sequence such that when *A* does something, what follows, or what probably follows, is an action by *B*. Thus, the statements about power could be translated into regular sequence. As to the difference between Professor Parsons and myself, which you pose very sharply, I hope that I did not say—I did not mean to say—that strictly causal notions are the only kinds of empirical statements that one can have in the study of politics. I understand that there are great bodies of the natural sciences where the notion of cause is not employed, where it is quite unnecessary. There are kinds of empirical statements that one makes in describing political systems where causal notions would not necessarily be inherent, but where some kind of functional relationship, which may leave the causal notion unspecified, would be present. For example, propositions asserting an association between high standards of living and democratic systems. Frequently this is put in causal terms, but I am not sure that there is any justification for doing so because we do not really know what the causal relationship is; all we know is that there is an association.

The real task of the political scientist is to talk about political systems, which implies that when we talk about them our object is to specify their defining characteristics. One of these defining characteristics is often said to be the distribution of power. So there is a need to be able to specify rather carefully what power is, simply to distinguish different kinds of political systems—in order, for example, to distinguish a pluralist system such as is alleged by some to exist in New Haven from a more monistic system such as is alleged to exist in Atlanta. But the task as I see it, assuming we can classify systems according to such categories, is to explain what conditions go along with the systems. They may be causal conditions; they may not.

QUESTION: You drew a very sharp distinction, I thought, between a correlation and a causal relationship. Now, on what basis do you make this distinction if your concept of cause is simply that A is always associated with B? Is it purely a temporal matter that B has to follow A? Or, if that is all there is to it, doesn't that get you into all kinds of trouble in complex relationships? In economics we constantly find that one thing appears to follow another, but a more fundamental analysis reveals that we are looking at the rate of change and that B actually precedes instead of following and so on. If you are basing the entire distinction between a correlation and causal relationship on time sequence, then I begin to wonder whether such an approach is very useful.

DAHL: I do not have any deep commitment as to what should distinguish a causal from other notions, but if there is any distinction at all, it is the sort of distinction that Braithwaite proposes. We can say that the advanced sciences do not even need the term "cause," but they go on using it. What does it mean? Braithwaite and others say that if anything, it means a regular sequence of a particular kind, namely, one in which there is temporal precedence.[13] We do not use the term for a functional relationship in which there is not temporal precedence in cause and effect.

QUESTION: It seems to me that there is a quite different concept of cause which is inadequately covered if you give the causal concept only an empirical reference. I think that a mathematical model builder would mean by causality that not only do you find that the mathematical model is supposed to explain reality—that is, that there is an empirical relationship between observables— but also that there is a logically necessary relationship between observables in terms of the particular model he is using for ex- planatory purposes. This would be regarded as the essential dis- tinction between an empirical correlation per se and a causal relationship in a system that includes both observation and a logical model of reality.

DAHL: This is a discussion of words. I would rule out logical necessity or else adopt a special term to distinguish it from cause. It seems to me that it is so radically different in character from cause in the empirical sense that it is absolutely important for clarity of analysis to keep the two separate.

QUESTION: I don't quite understand the difference between an empirical notion of cause and logical necessity. There is a three- fold sequence of how historians have used the word "cause." They first used it very simply to mean the one-to-one relationship. Then a number of particularly idealistic historians insisted that the notion was too crude and the word should be discarded. To- day a number of us have been arguing that if you discarded the word it kept creeping in through the back door because it was so built into everyday language, and our argument would be that the notion of cause is in the logical language rather than in anything we observe. In the course of trying to make common-

---

[13] Author's note. My answers here and after the next question now strike me as inadequate responses to the problems posed by my questioner. But I prefer to let them stand, not only from a desire to maintain the authenticity of discussion, but also because an adequate response might require another essay.

sense, ordinary explanations of what we see over the years, we use a causal form of discussion. Where is the difference between something empirical and a logical necessity built into ordinary language?

DAHL: You, as a historian, and your colleagues speak of the causes of the American Civil War. Now there is no logically necessary relationship there. It was not logically necessary that we have the Civil War in any meaningful sense of "logical necessity." You would like to know something about the antecedent conditions which you see as implying a regularly recurring relationship. The total combination may be such that the firing on Fort Sumter increased the probabilities of other kinds of actions, and this in turn increased the probability of Civil War. Now this is not logically necessary. There is a difference between saying on the one hand that all men are mortal, Socrates is a man, hence mortal (if the first two propositions are true then the conclusion is true) and saying that if Socrates is a man then he is mortal.

QUESTION: I agree. I do not think anybody today would talk about the causes of the Civil War. A historian would break it down into smaller compositions such as the firing on Fort Sumter inducing a succeeding event. Very closely related would be a generalization approaching almost a law of behavior which is usually understood and which would be the logical necessity. That is, the causal explanation would be, in terms of a logical necessity, mostly implicit.

DAHL: I find myself enthusiastically agreeing with you up to the very last sentence. Let me try an alternative to see if I can clarify the difference. The question of the role of explanation in history is a fascinating one. An analogy, it seems to me, is geology. Not long ago I asked several geologists to describe the process they go through when they explain something in geology. If I understood their answers, when they explain the origins of the Rocky Mountains they do exactly what you do: they break the answer down into subcategories, to regularities, and they have confidence in the regularities because of chemistry and perhaps biology. But they are not in my sense logical regularities. They are empirical regularities. So, too, when you begin looking at subsets of historical events you may look for explanation by drawing on empirical regularities of the kinds found in sociology or psychology.

QUESTION: Looking back to power for a moment, I think it might be fair to say that there are several basic types of problems that face power analysis today in political science. One is the problem of developing subordinate conceptualization: different types of power, different aspects of power, and the relationship between them. Another is the problem of measurement: various ways of locating and measuring power, and so on. A third might be to compare power structures in terms of their natures, or to explain what one found in the way of structure. As to measurement, we have standard lists of the various types of power measurements that prevail today: attribution and its various aspects, opinion-change method, attempts method, and so on; but there is no correlation between these measurements, and I would be inclined to suggest that the lack of correlation rests on very slim evidence. There may be more correlation than we think, and we should have more experimentation with regard to correlation. We may also need to develop more approaches to this problem. Do you have any suggestions as to new ways of measuring power, other than the more or less standard ones that we have had for some time; or are we up against a blank wall here?

DAHL: I can answer the second; I cannot really answer the first. I have a very strong feeling that we are not up against a blank wall. It sems to me that our study of power has progressed over the last few years in descriptive nicety. If it should turn out that there is not a high correlation, we would begin to move in the direction that you suggested a moment ago, of breaking the global notion into categories, so that in ten years' time the term "power" would leave our vocabulary. As to your initial question, I do not really have any specific answer, but I have a hunch that better ways of getting at this problem are going to turn up.

Some Notions on Causality and Teleology in Economics

Paul A. Samuelson

When I started to prepare this paper, I decided it would be wise to read the transcript of my predecessors in this series. In reading the words of a distinguished sociologist, a distinguished political scientist, a distinguished philosopher, and a distinguished expert in the mathematics of communication, I gained many bits of knowledge. But the most reassuring lesson I learned was that it would not be absolutely necessary to stick closely to the assigned subject. Causation apparently is one of those scaffoldings inside which you can build a sermon of almost any type.

I propose to discuss various problems of causality that arise in day-to-day economic research. There are numerous semantic problems connected with causality and I must confess they are not my major interest. And for the most part I shall be discussing causality with a small c, not cosmic causality with a large C. Thus, I shall be shamelessly begging all the deep epistemological questions connected with the subject, offering only as my feeble defense that most scientists and practical workers in the field find that if they beg fundamental questions there seem to be very few penalties for doing so.

WHO KILLED COCK ROBIN?

A typical semantic question arises whenever we have a whole chain of events that precede or lead up to an event. If *any* element of the chain were different or lacking, then a last event would not have happened the way it did happen. It is rather like electric switches arranged in series. Open but one switch and of course the current will not flow. So in economics, people used to debate seriously—I am afraid they still do—questions like the following: Does M, the amount of money, cause an increase in business activity and price levels? Or is it the change in the interest rate (or the structure of interest rates and degree of credit rationing) that is to be invariably associated with those changes in prices and activity? Lauchlin Currie wrote a book, *The Supply and Control of Money in the United States,* back in the early 1930s when I was a student. The ink was hardly dry before he had repudiated all its contents, but nobody told me that; and when I received the book with the dried ink, I had to wrestle with the question of whether after all it was not M that had really caused the change, since allegedly without the change in M there would not have been the change in interest rates to produce the final effect. A similar issue arose about a decade ago when Professor Milton Friedman of the University of Chicago and I found ourselves on the same panel testifying on money and banking before a Congressional Committee. I spelled out in great detail what I considered to be the mechanisms and sequences involved in attempts to affect the level of national income through use of federal reserve monetary policy. From the oral confrontation I could not tell whether there was agreement with this analysis; so when I got back to the office, I wrote a letter to Professor Friedman specifically asking whether there were any points at which our views were in variance. Being busy, he wrote back briefly that while he had no quarrel with my analysis, he considered it redundant. So long as a change in M can be counted upon to achieve the desired effect in the end, why bother to elucidate the intermediate steps involving the interest cost of loans and availability of credit? Friedman likened the discussion to a quarrel over whether it is the loss of blood, the bullet of the murder weapon, the gun itself, the finger that pulled the trigger, or the gunman who kills the victim.[1] So long as we can be sure that death

---

[1] In some traditions a responsible and free human agent has to be regarded as the "cause" of anything. When Professor Jacob Viner and I served on the advisory board to the Commission on Money and Credit, I was interested to hear him remark that there was good precedent in the fields of jurisprudence and torts to lay any possible blame for postwar inflation upon the Federal Reserve Board rather than on such factors as the backlog of demand or level of public debt, since "they" were the responsible agents whose duty it was to prevent the evil.

will "follow" the "initial" act, why quibble about the details? And the same goes for monetary policy: so long as an engineered change in M can be counted on not to induce an offsetting opposite change in the "velocity of circulation of money," Friedman prefers to skip the intervening stages.

I am not much interested in the semantic problem of isolating one or more "causes" in a complex of causes, and at this late hour I don't suppose you are either. If there is agreement on the facts, that we do face something like a sequence of switches in series and that any one open switch will break the circuit, there is nothing left to argue about. And actually some of the reasons debates continue are not methodological at all, even though they may appear to be. Thus, I probably do not have Friedman's confidence that the gun will invariably kill the victim. More specifically, what is usually defined as an increase in M, if it is brought about by open-market operations, which in deep depression give people more cash and take away from them infinitesimal-yielding treasury bills that are close money substitutes, I should not expect to have anything like the appreciable effect on employment, total spending, and production that a massive gold find would have during a boom year. Similarly, some economists might think Currie right to have emphasized M and not interest rates, if they hold the theory that it is wealth-effects which are important for total spending and not interest rates.

LIGHTNING CAUSES THUNDER?

In considering complications introduced by multiple causes, the above discussion runs ahead of the story. The simplest sense in which an economist or anyone else would understand causation lies in the motto: *post hoc, ergo propter hoc.* I call this a motto but of course it is usually dubbed a fallacy. Yet no one would have had occasion to label it a fallacy if it did not already suggest some germ of truth. Leave out the word *ergo* and you are left with the unsophisticated notion that whenever A happens, B always (sometimes, or usually) happens soon afterward. A is the cause of the B that happens soon after it. Indeed in the previous section of my talk my tongue could hardly avoid the question-begging word "antecedent." This asymmetry of time is thus often regarded as the key test for causation. My bullet penetrates the heart (or his heart sucks in my bullet, it does not matter) and *then* mine enemy bleeds. Two elastic billiard balls collide and then they rebound from each other.

This time sequence of events seems to be reduced down to an irreducible unit, which must be accepted. True, we can put a fast camera on the happenings and play back the record in slow motion. But no matter how fast our cameras, all we can do ultimately is record the happenings as they play themselves out—the first contact of the balls, the bending of the surfaces, their subsequent snapping back, and so forth. Only in the fairy tales of elementary physics books do rebounds take place instantaneously. All we can say is that a detailed set of pictures will reveal the billiard balls going through their appointed waltz. We can hope to describe the process in greater or less detail. But in no ultimate sense can we "explain" the process. Nor, as David Hume showed long ago, can we ever "prove" its logical necessity or empirical inevitability.

I have been using loose language in saying that the effect takes place some time after the cause. How much time later? The process is continuous and no matter how small we make the time interval, it can, in principle, be made smaller still. There appear to be no irreducible instants involved in the notion of causality. (This has led some economic theorists to insist upon taking the limit and replacing a difference-equation formulation by a differential-equation formulation, a topic which will be touched on later.) True we can give more interesting descriptions that will cover many cases other than that of colliding billiard balls. And we may be able to correlate the description of how the ball bounces with a description of what happens under a microscope to various molecular interactions. But, like Margaret Fuller, or Newton looking at a falling apple, in the last analysis we must merely accept the universe.

It is not always easy to identify the true cause of an effect. Is it witchcraft or arsenic that kills the rats? Is it the tobacco or the paper which increases the probability of lung cancer? Because economists cannot employ controlled experiments, our problems of identification are difficult ones. Occasionally, we can hope to observe a cause so dramatic that it stands out like a physicist's controlled-experiment causes: a massive tax cut or dominating war incident may provide a worthy case for intensive study and follow-up. But such opportunities are exceptional. I am sure that I am not alone among social scientists (and meteorologists and cosmogonists) who confess to a certain *Schadenfreude* over the plight of medical scientists in trying to decide whether smoking as such is harmful to health and longevity. "Mere statistical association can prove nothing about cause and effect," the purists aver. "Instead of X causing Y, they may both be the effect of some common Z." True enough, but remember, nothing can prove anything about an empirical regularity. All one can ever hope to do about an empirical invariance is recognize it and describe it. To say: "X is not the 'genuine cause' of Y but Z is" is merely to say: "Z and Y are more invariantly correlated empirically than are X and Y." I know that some will find the above sentence a startling one, but it is time they learn to face the facts of life.

Difficult problems of timing are often involved. When we see lightning before hearing thunder, we may falsely infer that the first caused the second. But more careful examination will reveal that sound travels sufficiently slower than light to account for both being the simultaneous accompaniment of an electric discharge. Particularly in case of business cycle oscillations, it is often hard to know whether one time series is turning down before the crowd or is belatedly following the crowd's previous cyclical downturn. Of this, an example is provided by money M and national output Y. Historically, M has lagged behind Y at turning points. Crude cause and effect would then lead to the inference that Y is cause and M effect. But those who want to reverse the direction of causation can always take foolish comfort in the fact that the *rate of growth* of M, dM/dt, will for a quasi-sinusoidal fluctuation turn down one-quarter cycle before M itself—and thus the causal sequence $dM/dt \rightarrow Y$ may help save the appearances.

Molière's listeners laugh at the notion that morphine puts one to sleep because of its "soporific" quality. But whom is the joke on? Strike out the word "because" as I have suggested you strike out the word "*ergo*" in the *post hoc* phrase and you are left with the important recognition of a regularity. For, never forget that morphine does put one to sleep and coffee does not. And the chemist working to produce a new drug does seek a compound with the sleep-inducing quality of morphine but without its "addicting" quality.

DIFFERENCE EQUATIONS

To a mathematical economist, the crudest notion of cause and effect involves a time lag and could be depicted by a simple difference equation, such as

$$(1) \qquad Y(t+1) = f[X(t)] \qquad \text{or} \qquad X(t+1) = F[X(t)]$$

In the first case we have some functional relation that tells us what is the effect on Y at time $t + 1$ when one period *earlier* X took place at t. This first case still leaves us with two unknowns and only one relation; so the answer is indeterminate. Until we are somehow given knowledge of the arbitrary function $X(t)$, we cannot solve to know $Y(t+1)$. Of course in the simplest chain, we might have $X(t)$ depending causally in turn on some third, still prior variable $Z(t-1)$. This, as in the search for a first cause or in the proof of God's existence, can lead to an infinite regress. All our yesterdays had a yesterday.

The second form of the causal relation closes the circle. The behavior of the system now depends upon its own immediate past. Now the system is almost determinate, the number of our functional equations being equal to the number of our unknown time-sequence variables. What we need to get a determinate system is arbitrary knowledge of the initial condition of X at some arbitrary beginning of time: given $X(t^{\circ})$, repeated use of the F function will give us $X(t)$ for all subsequent time periods, $t > t^{\circ}$.

Particularly in the field of business cycles, such autonomous and timeless difference-equation models have been frequently employed these last thirty years. A typical example is the case of the cobweb fluctuations of a farm price, as farmers produce this period a high crop if last period's price was high, thereby giving rise to a series of oscillations in output and price that may or may not damp down to equilibrium. Such names as Tinbergen, Frisch, Kahn, Clark, Lundberg, Robertson, Samuelson, Domar, Metzler, and Hicks have been associated with such model sequences. I shall give only some trivial examples here.

Logistic population

Malthus thought population would, if unchecked, grow biologically at a constant percentage rate per period. In effect he stipulated the hypothetical linear causal system

$$X(t+1) = a\, X(t)$$

where a can be set about equal to 2 if a generation of about a quarter of a century is used as the time period. But Malthus also believed in the law of diminishing returns: we can represent this by saying that the percentage increase in population on a fixed acreage of land declines as the size and density of the population increases. If the law of decline is linear in X, we get the finite-difference form of the Verhulst-Pearl logistic model of population

$$(2) \quad \frac{X(t+1) - X(t)}{X(t)} = b - c\, X(t) \qquad b>0,\ c>0,\ X(t) \geqq 0$$

While the exact solution to this cannot be expressed in terms of tabulated elementary functions, the system is determined in its behavior once we know an initial non-negative value for $X(t^{*})$. And it is easy to show that there are two equilibrium levels for the system: the zero level, where it never changes at all, but which is unstable once any positive population leads to a Malthusian explosion away from zero; and the asymptotic level $X = b/c$, where returns have been diminished so much that the net balance of births over deaths is zero. This upper equilibrium is locally stable, and can be shown to be returned to from initial disturbances above or below it.[2]

If a single variable depends causally upon its own state just a single period earlier, it cannot display a very rich variety of behavior. Even if the law of dependence is nonlinear, the system must either approach an equilibrium or diverge to infinity; a first-order system cannot, by its nature, oscillate (except in a simple, every-other-period way). However, if we reinterpret the symbol $X(t)$ to be a whole vector of different variables, and $F[X(t)]$ to be a whole set of functional dependences—one for each variable, giving its present level in determinate dependence upon *all* the other variables at the previous period—we get a simple causal system which can show richer variety of behavior. (And we also automatically cover the case where a variable depends upon its values at several earlier periods.)

Oscillations in the struggle for existence

Thus, let $X(t)$ stand for $[y_1(t), y_2(t)]$, where y_1 stands for the population of edible deer and y_2 the population of predatory humans. Adapting the simple fables of Lotka and Volterra[3] on the struggle for existence between two species, let us postulate that deer, y_1, would follow a Malthus-logistic law if vile man were at the level $y_2 = 0$. But suppose that each increment of hunters y_2 reduces deer's percentage growth rate by a constant amount, d. And now let us postulate that the percentages rate of increase of man increases by a constant amount for each increment of

[2] P. A. Samuelson, *Foundations of Economic Analysis*, (Cambridge: Harvard University Press, 1947), disscusses these matters in Part II and Mathematical Appendix B. For b and c small enough, as when we use short periods in (2), the stability assertions hold.

[3] A. J. Lotka, *Elements of Mathematical Biology*, (Baltimore: Williams and Wilkins, 1925; New York: Dover, 1956,), 89; V. Volterra, *Leçons sur la theorie mathématique de la lutte pour la vie*, (Paris: Gauthier-Villers, 1931). In addition to this summary of Volterra's post-1926 work, see for a summary of his post-1936 results relevant to the calculus of variations, "Principes de biologie mathématique," *Acta Biotheoretica*, V. III (1937), reproduced in Volterra, *Opere Matematiche*, V, 414-47.

deer per capita: i.e., plentiful enough venison means human population growth. Our system can now be written as

$$\frac{y_1(t+1) \; - \; y_1(t)}{y_1(t)} = b \; - \; cy_1(t) \; - \; dy_2(t)$$

(3)

$$\frac{y_2(t+1) \; - \; y_2(t)}{y_2(t)} = -e \; + \; g\frac{y_1(t)}{y_2(t)}$$

While this system is so simple that it could be thought up and written down in a matter of seconds, no mathematician can write down its explicit solution in terms of known elementary functions. Still, mathematics assures us of its unique solution, which for any initial conditions can be rapidly computed. Also, mathematical analysis and common sense enable us to assert many of its simple properties:

1. If both species begin at zero, they stay at zero.
2. If man begins at zero but deer are positive, deer will grow alone in the Malthus-logistic fashion.
3. If man begins without deer for food, he will move toward extinction (in accordance with the negative-signed coefficient e).
4. If both are positive but man is scarce, deer will multiply. Before they reach their saturation level, man will multiply and almost certainly (for c sufficiently small) there will be an overshoot of human population, which will subsequently kill off many deer, leading in turn to a great decimation of men. This goes on until men are again scarce compared to deer, and we are off qualitatively on another cycle.
5. There is a critical density of deer and men around which the system will oscillate, derived by setting the left-hand sides of (3) equal to zero and solving the resulting linear equation for the equilibrium level of (y_1,y_2) that will be self-perpetuating.

Cause and Effect

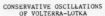

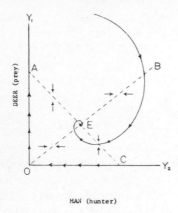

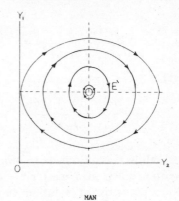

Figure 1
(from equation 4)

Figure 2
(from equation 5)

Figure 1 shows the equilibrium point *E* at which the system could settle down. Why must there be such a point? From the second equation for human growth, we know that human population will be stationary along some line of balanced per capita food, namely *OEB*. Above that line, deer are so abundant that men will increase (as shown by the fact that all arrows above the line point westward). Below the line all arrows point eastward as men die out from shortage of food.

On the other hand, it must be obvious that deer cannot grow indefinitely to ever higher levels, for two reasons. The first involves the law of diminishing returns, as indicated by the depressing *c* coefficient in the first equation. The second involves the fact that numerous hunters will kill off deer. The curve of balance, where deer growth turns into decay, is shown by the curve *AEC*: above it deer decline as shown by the southward-pointing arrow; below it, deer increase back toward it. If deer are stationary on *AEC*, and men are stationary on *OEB*, then, at their intersection point *E* both are stationary and we have an equilibrium point.

Actually, the equilibrium point eventually will be attained by the system from any point that starts out with both species. The equilibrium point is thus "stable," with all swings around it being ultimately damped down and spiraling into the stationary state E.

I shall not give rigorous mathematical proof of these assertions (which are valid for a rather wide choice of positive constants). But let me now consider some alternative formulations of the problem. Suppose we let the time period be cut in half from 1 to ½; then to be cut in half again, each time writing out some idealized difference equations purporting to show the laws of population development. In the limit, as the time period shrinks to zero, if we let terms like $[y_1(t + \triangle t) - y_1(t)]/\triangle t$ go the limit as $\triangle t$ goes to zero, we replace our finite time differences by derivatives, which we may write as $dy_1(t)/dt$ or $\dot{y}_1$. The adapted Lotka-Volterra system (3) then might become the differential equation system

$$\frac{\dot{y}_1}{y_2} = B - Cy_1 - Dy_2$$

(4)

$$\frac{\dot{y}_2}{y_2} = -E + G\frac{y_2}{y_1}$$

If these new coefficients are related properly to the old, Figure 1 will still give a picture of the resulting motions. In fact, the continuous trajectories of the figure are really more appropriate for this differential-equation formulation than for the difference-equation formulation. Actually to depict (3) accurately in Figure 1, I should have used a set of discrete dots, or used straight-line segments or arrows in showing the move from one period's position to the next period's.

To tie this discussion up with the usual Lotka-Volterra model and pave the way for the later issue of time reversibility, I should mention that most such writers do not take account of diminishing returns or the problem of density of food to hunter. Their simplest equations take the form

$$\frac{\dot{y}_1}{y_1} = a_1 - a_{12}\, y_2$$

(5)

$$\frac{\dot{y}_2}{y_2} = -a_2 + a_{21}\, y_1$$

It is not hard to show that these give rise to Figure 2's closed oscillations, corresponding to a *perpetuum mobile* around the equilibrium level E'. These "conservative oscillations," which neither damp down nor build up amplitude in anti-damped fashion, resemble the swings of frictionless pendulums so beloved of classical mechanics. (Later I shall show important differences for teleology between the conservative and dissipative cases.)

DERIVATIVES OR DIFFERENCES?

Does reality dictate that true causal analysis should be thrown into the form of "cause now creating effect later," requiring us to use a difference-equation formulation like that of (1) or (3)? Or, since time intervals can be cut down as much as we like, does reality call for a differential-equation formulation like that of (4) or (5)? Some economists and scientists have acted as if such a question has a unique answer. In economics, I believe Richard M. Goodwin has argued that events take place in finite time and our observations come in discrete intervals, and that therefore in principle a difference-equation formulation is optimal. Against this, economists such as R. F. Harrod have asserted the equally one-sided view that derivative flows are somehow more fundamental than lagged differences. Most of modern physics involves use of Newtonian derivatives and partial derivatives. At least one physicist, perhaps influenced by the conceptual importance of the quantum theory, has proposed that all physics be recast in terms of finite differences; and my old teacher, E. B. Wilson, the last student of Willard Gibbs and himself a distinguished mathematical physicist and statistician, once told me that Gibbs mentioned, in his last years, an attempt to express as much as possible in terms of finite differences.

In a sense, the quarrel is an empty one, involving unimportant semantic distinctions. In a sense, the answer can be arbitrary, depending upon the convenience of the investigator. In a sense, both of the suggested optimal solutions are wrong. Let me explain.

If we deal with analytic functions possessing Taylor's expansions, a difference equation could be written as an infinite series of differential equations. Conversely, in finding the actual solutions of differential equations, as in exterior ballistics, the usual methods of numerical approximation involve using difference equations to achieve any desired degree of accuracy. So it would seem that there is not much to choose between the two devices. Either or both will often do. And, as will be seen, each is but a special case of the more general use of "functionals," in which the position of a system now and forever depends upon all its past behavior.

"Hysteresis" phenomena

For, if we really go back to a detailed picturing of the colliding billiard balls, we realize that at best all we can observe is that the present position of the system is in a determinate relationship to *all* of its past behavior. When we come to divide time most meticulously, we usually do not conclude with a simple, low-order differential equation. When we come to abandon our difference equations for a more exact description, we seem to end up with some causal law that has to be written as a functional of past behavior. We must now go back and rewrite the difference equations of (1) not as a simple differential equation but rather as the following functionals

$$(1)' \qquad Y(t) = f \left| \begin{matrix} s=t \\ t : x(s) \\ s=-\infty \end{matrix} \right| \quad \text{or} \quad X(t) = F \left| \begin{matrix} s=t \\ t : X(s) \\ s=-\infty \end{matrix} \right|$$

The first says that the *behavior of an effect* Y *at time* t *depends upon the whole shape of behavior at all previous times of its cause* X. The second example is one of a closed or complete causal system in which the present of a system is uniquely determined by *all* of its past. The struggle for existence was a good example to use since Volterra has set down a simple model of "hysteresis type" (which remembers and depends upon its detailed past), of which the following is a simple instance

$$\dot{y}_1 = y_1(a_1 + a_{12}y_2 + \int_0^t F_{12}(t-s)y_2(s)ds)$$

(5)′

$$\dot{y}_2 = y_2(a_2 + a_{21}y_1 + \int_0^t F_{21}(t-s)y_1(s)ds)$$

The last integrals are among the simplest functionals that take account of "hereditary" influences of all the past. If the $F_{ij}(x)$ functions are certain simple sums of polynomial-exponential terms, of the form $t^k e \lambda^{jt}$, the system may be capable of being written as an ordinary differential equation of high order. If the F_{ij} memory functions are all damped down toward zero, the system will behave rather like a causal system and unlike the actual stream of history, of which the Bible says, "We pass this way only once." When the equilibrium of a system depends on (and is dictated) by its path toward equilibrium, the scientist has an uncomfortable feeling.

Examples of differences and derivatives

I do not want to gloss over the difference between differential- and difference-equation systems. Galileo's studies of falling bodies paved the way for Newtonian dynamics; but for his problem Galileo did not really need the concepts of the infinitesimal calculus. For slow motions of a falling ball on a smooth inclined plane, Galileo could record the distance the ball traveled in t periods after it started from rest, in the accompanying table.

Observations on Falling Body (Galileo)

Time	t	0	1	2	3	4	$\dots n \dots$
Distance	$S = f(t)$	0	1	4	9	16	$\dots n^2 \dots$
Average speed	$\dfrac{f(t+1)-f(t)}{1}$	1	3	5	7	9 $\dots$	$\dots 2n+1 \dots$
Instantaneous speed	$\dot{S} = \dfrac{df(t)}{dt}$	0	2	4	6	8	$\dots 2n$

In this hypothetical table, since the unit of time and the unit of distance is at my disposal, I have arbitrarily assumed that Galileo uses as his unit of distance for the experiment the distance covered in the first arbitrary time period. He discovered that this distance would, of course, differ with the angle of the inclined plane but (in contradiction to Aristotle) would not depend upon the "heaviness" of the ball. Since we still have the time unit at our disposal, we can assume it selected so that the ball (which is to anyone's eye obviously speeding up) travels exactly twice as far in the second period as in the first. However, after the first three entries in the second row of the table are filled in, there is nothing to do but complete the rest according to nature's testimony.

The remarkable fact emerges that nature's entries follow a very simple law or formula, and will be the same for any size ball and (in terms of these adjusted units) for any angle of inclination. Galileo knew the basic rule that the distance is proportional to the square of the time. This pattern is a logical implication of the fact that "the distance traversed in *each* time period grows as the odd numbers grow," like 1, 3, 5, 7, . . . as shown in the third row of the table. Or, what is the same thing, if we call the distance covered in each single time period its average speed, "the average speed is proportional to the time, growing from one time period to the next by a constant amount," which we know is proportional to the fundamental constant of gravity. (I have not yet called it an acceleration constant because I still want to avoid Newtonian calculus.) Symbolically, Galileo's law for a falling body can be summarized by

$$(6) \qquad \left\{ \frac{[S(t+1)-S(t)]}{1} - \frac{[S(t)-S(t-1)]}{1} \right\} = \Delta^2 S = +c$$

The fourth row of the table introduces the Newtonian notion of instaneous speed, which is the limiting average speed as the time interval shrinks to zero without limit. It too is proportional to t, a fact about which both Galileo and Descartes were confused simply because of logical errors on their part. (They thought it proportional to distance $s(t)$ rather than to $\sqrt{s(t)}$.)

Using the concept of first and second derivatives for instantaneous speed and acceleration, we can express Galileo's law in alternative differential equation form

$$(7) \qquad \frac{d^2S(t)}{dt^2} = +C$$

where C and c are closely related but not quite identical. And only with the concept of instantaneous speed could Galileo have formulated the later law of conservation of energy: kinetic energy plus potential energy always equals a constant, or

$$(8) \qquad (ds/dt)^2 + (-2S) \equiv 0$$

When Newton saw the apple fall, he was not led merely to rediscover Galileo's rule. The point of this not completely apocryphal incident is that Newton realized that the moon and Kepler's planets behaved *like* the falling apple in terms of the laws of gravity. However, even in the simplest case of the earth going around the sun in an elliptical Keplerian orbit, as if its acceleration is inversely proportional to the square of the distance between it and the sun, we need differential equations like

$$(9) \qquad \frac{d^2x_1}{dt^2} = \frac{m_1m_2}{\sqrt{x_1^2+x_2^2}} \quad , \quad \frac{d^2x_2}{dt^2} = \frac{m_1m_2}{\sqrt{x_1^2+x_2^2}}$$

and cannot summarize this behavior in any simple difference equation system

$$(10) \qquad x_i(t+1) = F^i[x_1(t),x_2(t), \ldots] \qquad (i=1,2, \ldots)$$

Only after we have named two instantaneous magnitudes of the Newtonian type, $x_3 = dx_1/dt$ and $x_4 = dx_2/dt$ can equations (10) be put in the vector form $dX/dt = F(X)$ and solved to give $X(t) = G[t;X(t_0)]$ and, eventually, in what appears to be the difference-equation form $X(t+1) = G[1;X(t)]$. Without being able to define the final two instantaneous velocities, we could attribute no meaning to these last difference equations.

FROM LAPLACE'S WORLD EQUATION TO MARKOV'S PROBABILITY MATRIX

Newtonian mechanics led Laplace to believe that the whole universe could be described by a world equation of the (vector) form $dX/dt = F(X)$. He boasted that given these laws of causality and the initial conditions of the universe at any instant of time, he could, in principle, predict the whole future in all of its details. When Napolean asked Laplace, "What is the role of God in your system?", the illustrious writer of *Celestial Mechanics* replied, "Sire, I have no need for that hypothesis." (On hearing of this, Lagrange, who has been called the Shakespeare of mathematics, is supposed to have said, "Yes, but what a beautiful hypothesis it is.")

Note that the Laplacean causal system is in differential-equation form and makes no use of any time interval between antecedent cause and subsequent effect. How paradoxical that this most ideal case of a causal system has no asymmetry of time connected with it at all!

The position of the universe determines its own motions at the instant, and thus forever. As far as the mathematics is concerned, there are no time lags involved. And the same existence theorems that guarantee the uniqueness of a determinate solution forward in time also guarantees its existence backward in time. Just as we can know where the earth will be five minutes or millennia from now, we can know where it must have been five minutes or millennia ago.

What has just been said is true of *any* set of differential equa-

tions. Thus, it is just as true of my damped struggle-for-existence
system (4) as it is for the standard Lotka-Volterra system (5).

We can run the motion picture backward in Figures 1 and
2, reversing the direction of the arrows. However, the undamped
L-V system of Figure 2 shows conservative oscillations that look
essentially the same backward as forward, the only difference
being the inessential one that a clockwise motion is converted
into a counterclockwise one. This can be seen from the structure
of (5). Making the substitution $t = -T$ gives essentially the same
differential equations in terms of the new, reversed time variable
T, except that the human hunter now acts as if he were the prey,
and the deer now appears to be the predator.

In conservative mechanics we have the same true time reversibility. Thus, if we consider the case of a truly frictionless pendulum, which is undergoing swings so limited as to be considered
simple harmonic motion, we get for its dynamics the differential
equation

(11) $$\frac{d^2y}{dt^2} + my = 0$$

On the other hand, if we introduce a little viscous friction,
the pendulum follows the more realistic equation.

(12) $$\frac{d^2y}{dt^2} + a\frac{dy}{dt} + my = 0$$

where $a > 0$ depicts the dampening effect of the deceleration from
the friction attributable to velocity. This last formulation departs
from the conservation of energy condition of classical mechanics,
as the forces of friction lead to the creation of heat. No longer
is it true that the sum of kinetic energy and potential energy
remains constant. In order to save the law of conservation of
energy, the physicists must introduce the new entity of thermal

energy. This is not, however, merely a case of juggling the books, creating a fictitious balancing item in order to save appearances. The First Law of Thermodynamics, discovered by Joule and Mayer in the first half of the nineteenth century, does note a strong regularity of cause and effect, namely that the same amount of mechanical energy always gets converted into the same amount of thermal energy.

IS TIME REALLY REVERSIBLE?

Here we encounter a paradox of time reversibility that is very relevant to the problem of effect following cause. Early writers such as Count Rumford felt that heat must reflect the kinetic energies of molecules in motion at a level that the eye cannot observe. Clausius, Maxwell, Boltzmann, and finally Willard Gibbs tried to develop a kinetic theory related to statistical mechanics. The same formal laws of Newtonian-Lagrangean-Hamiltonian mechanics were now to be applied to a vast assemblage of molecules. It turned out, after such writers as G. D. Birkhoff, B. O. Koopman, J. von Neumann, N. Wiener, and E. Hopf had, by means of the "ergodic theorem," cleared up some of the difficulties of logical analysis, that the classical mechanics of this extended assemblage of molecules still had the intrinsic time reversibility properties of the frictionless pendulum. While none of this caused any great problems for the First Law of Thermodynamics relating to the law of conservation of energy, it did pose serious problems for the Second Law of Thermodynamics. Clausius and Kelvin had formulated this law as requiring that a magnitude called "entropy" should increase asymmetrically in time. My Figure 1 case, in which things settle down rather than oscillate conservatively, is the more indicated image.

At this point, classical thermodynamics became less convenient than kinetic theory and statistical mechanics. Boltzmann interpreted entropy in terms of probability, much as is done today in information theory. Instead of saying that my cream is certain to mix with my coffee, cooling it and being heated by it until they are in temperature equilibrium, probability says that it is very likely indeed that this will happen but that by chance alone the two substances *might* separate out again and display diverging temperatures.

The paradox connected with time irreversibility did not disappear completely with the introduction of probability. True, if our cards are well shuffled I shall I shall be surprised to see thirteen spades come in my next hand of bridge. But I should be just as surprised to have the same mixed hand come up next time as came up last time. Curiously enough, one of the most interesting reconciliations of these difficulties connected with time reversibility of cause and effect in a mechanical system comes from abandoning tight causality in favor of a probability model. The most celebrated one was given half a century ago by P. and T. Ehrenfest, and is described in M. Kac, *Probability and Related Topics in Physical Sciences* (N. Y., Interscience, 1959), Chapter 3.

Number 100 balls from 1 to 100. Divide them into two boxes. Now pick by some symmetric random device any number from 1 to 100. Suppose the number that comes up is 17; then move the ball 17 to the other box. Continue this process, always moving the ball whose number has come up. What happens to the number of balls in each box? It should be intuitively obvious that there is a tendency for the numbers to become equal at 50 each. Why? Because the box which at any time has the greater number of balls is more likely to have one of its numbers picked by the sampling device and hence is more likely to lose a ball. From him who hath shall (more likely!) be taken away, which, as every Bible reader knows, results in a "tendency" toward equality.

This Ehrenfest model is an example of what has come to be known as a Markov transitional probability matrix. In the mid-1930s such concepts were not fashionable in American statistics courses, although now, thanks to W. Feller's classic text, *An Introduction to Probability Theory and Its Applications,* New York, Wiley, 1950), they are popular. While thinking about F. W. Taussig's data showing that the sons of businessmen were much more likely to become businessmen than were the sons of farmers or laborers, I was led as a young student to rediscover the concept of a transitional probability matrix. It was with wonderment that I inferred the theorem that the transition probabilities for grandsons of businessmen and other social classes followed the simple rules of matrix multiplication or squaring, and likewise for still later generations.[4]

Probability matrices have become very popular in modern econometrics. Just as Laplace had the rather grandiose notion of a causal world equation, bold scholars like Guy Orcutt of the University of Wisconsin have dreamt of determining empirically for the economic system a grand stochastic probability matrix, which would give information like the following: The chance of a bachelor's becoming a married father is q per cent, and the chance of his buying a car is p per cent. The future of the world would not be exactly determinate, but its probability laws would

[4] See P. A. Samuelson, *Economics* (New York: McGraw-Hill, 1964, 6th ed.) 125, n. 1, for the following brief description: "The arithmetic of 'transition probabilities' can be made to yield the following results. Divide society into two classes, so that I am either a U in the Upper class or a *non*-U in the Lower. If a child's chance to move out of his parents' class is as great as to stay in, then ½ the children, grandchildren, great-grandchildren, and descendants generally of a U parent will be U's. But if there is social stratification so that a child has only ¼ chance of moving into a class different from his parents, ¾ ($= ½ + ¼$) of the children of U's will be U's. However, it can be deduced that only ⅝ ($= ½ + ⅛$) of grandchildren of U's will be U's; and only $9/16$ ($= ½ + 1/16$) of their greatgrandchildren. Evidently, the chance of remote descendants of U's being also U's goes ultimately down to ½ [the ergodic state], with 50 per cent of the excess above the ½ equality level wiped out at each new generation."

This quotation explains in words the following matrix identity, where the probability ¾ is written as $1/2 + s/2$, with $s = 1/2$

$$
\begin{bmatrix} \dfrac{1}{2} + \dfrac{s}{2} & \dfrac{1}{2} - \dfrac{s}{2} \\[2mm] \dfrac{1}{2} - \dfrac{s}{2} & \dfrac{1}{2} + \dfrac{s}{2} \end{bmatrix}^{n} = \begin{bmatrix} \dfrac{1}{2} + \dfrac{s^{n}}{2} & \dfrac{1}{2} - \dfrac{s^{n}}{2} \\[2mm] \dfrac{1}{2} - \dfrac{s^{n}}{2} & \dfrac{1}{2} + \dfrac{s^{n}}{2} \end{bmatrix}
$$

As $n \to \infty$, all probabilities $\to 1/2$, the ergodic state for this doubly-stochastic matrix.

be exactly determinate in such a model. I know some readers will wince when I use the words "exact" and "probability" in the same sentence. But I see no contradiction: there are many models in which the probability laws are specified with exactitude, with only the sample outcome being left to chance. Often, in these models, as the size of the sample becomes large, certain probabilities approach unity in value, which is an exact statement even though it does not purport to express a "certainty" of actual outcome.

DETERMINISM VERSUS FREE WILL?

The notion of a causally determinate world was depressing to many nineteenth century students of science. The materialism of physics seemed to grind out any role for the free exercise of the human spirit. Along with Percy Bridgman and many exponents of logical positivism, I have not been able to find much conceptually refutable meaning to this debate: what difference does it make if one believes in one side or the other? All facts fit in equally well or equally badly. (If I claim to have chosen not to fly on the plane that crashed yesterday, my opponent can claim that this choice was preordained.)

Yet many physicists and laymen thought that the discovery of radioactivity and of quantum mechanics broke the spell of mere causality and reopened the way for free will. This view seems rather odd. It is true that many of the models of quantum mechanics do involve magnitudes called probabilities, but what has that to do with the question of whether that murderer in the dock was free to have led an upright rather than dissolute life? Note, too, that many of the theories are mathematically exact in their determination of probability laws. Finally, and this seems to be enormously important and yet commonly overlooked, *quantum mechanics has introduced some of the strongest regularities into physics that have ever been discovered.* Just as earlier physics stated the strong laws that one cannot build a perpetual motion machine of the first or of the second type, quantum theory says one cannot ever determine simultaneously with complete accuracy the position and velocity of a certain particle. The strongest laws of nature, which limit what one can expect to observe, are just such impossibility laws. And far from lessening their number, it seems to me that quantum mechanics has increased it.

CONSERVATION OF ENERGY IN ECONOMICS?

Why should a person interested in economics for its own sake spend time considering conservative oscillations of mechanics? Experience suggests that our dynamic problems in economics have something in common with those of the physical or biological *sciences*. But, as I long ago indicated,[5] it is not useful to get "bogged down in the research for economic concepts corresponding to mass, energy, momentum, force, and space." And I may add that the sign of a crank or half-baked speculator in the social sciences is his search for something in the social system that corresponds to the physicist's notion of "entropy."

The ecological system of Figure 2 appears to satisfy a law like the conservation of energy equation of (8). But this is true mainly because Lotka and Volterra set up an overly simple razor's-edge case. If we were to add to the first equation of (5) a tiny term $-hy_1$, to reflect diminishing returns (or $+hy_1$ for increasing returns), Figure 2 would begin to look like Figure 1 and show damped (or explosive) oscillations that run into (or out of) the equilibrium point. But it would be quite uninformative to explain this by a physics concept of friction or to try to save the appearance of a conservation-of-energy law by creating a fictitious form of dissipated thermal energy.

Of course, if Lotka or Volterra were alive, they might defend their razor's-edge conservative oscillations by an appeal to experience. The jungle and the sea do both display a *perpetuum mobile*, in which prey and predator fluctuate in numbers over the years.

---

[5] See P. A. Samuelson, *Foundations of Economic Analysis* (Cambridge: Harvard University Press, 1947), Chapter XI, 311, where reference is made to the 1943 article in the *Review of Economic Statistics Festschrift* issue for Joseph A. Schumpeter (1943), 58-61.

One year deer abound; another year they are decimated. Attempts have even been made to do for ecology what econometricians do for economics, namely evaluate by statistical methods the parameters of the model. And Lotka and Volterra might argue, as M. Kalecki [6] has done, that the fact of *nondying-out and non-exploding oscillations* calls for a specification of a model which, like (5) and unlike (4) is neither damped nor antidamped and which does obey a conservation law. I believe such a defense is misguided for the following reasons.

As Malthus well knew, the struggle for existence does lead to fluctuations around the bare subsistence level. But the system is not an isolated and stationary one. It is the exogenous fluctuation in the weather—in rain and sun and flood and lightning—that causes fluctuations in crops and in numbers. In the false glow of an unusual harvest, species multiply; and they pay the price when chance brings the weather back to normal or below.

Just as Ehrenfest and other physicists had to add probability to the causal systems of physics to get around the time-reversibility feature of classical mechanics that was so inconsistent with the time asymmetry of the Second Law of Thermodynamics, so we must, in the interests of realism, add stochastic or probability disturbances to our economic and biological causal systems. Thus, systems (4) or (5) now take the general form

(13)

$$\dot{y}_1 = f_1(y_1, y_2) + u_1(t)$$
$$\dot{y}_2 = f_2(y_1, y_2) + u_2(t)$$

where the $u_i(t)$ are exogenous stochastic disturbances subject to whatever probability laws are appropriate to the weather or to technical innovations and political events.

---

[6] See *Foundations, op. cit.,* 337 for my critique of the Kalecki insistence upon conservative oscillations.

It can be shown that superimposing such random fluctuations on a conservative system of the Lotka-Volterra or frictionless-pendulum type will not lead to the factually correct observations of fluctuation that show *no historical trend in amplitude*. On the contrary, a conservative system "remembers" forever, so to speak, each shock it has ever received; and as time passes, it has more and more shocks to remember. In consequence of this, we have to predict that its future position will wander further from any equilibrium point.

So what the facts of a "stationary time series" call for is precisely the reverse of the Lotka-Volterra-Kalecki case. My damped pattern of (4) and Figure 1 has the property that each past shock is, so to speak, gradually forgotten. Thus, as time passes and more exogenous shocks are experienced, we reach an "ergodic state," where the new shocks are just enough to balance out the forgetting of old shocks. This has the following meaning: If I begin by knowing where the system is in Figure 1, I can then specify tight probability limits on where it will be a little later, because only a few $u_i(t)$ shocks can be registered in that interval. If I try to predict for a longer time T ahead, my probability guesses widen. But, and this is the point, they do not widen indefinitely; instead, they approach a limiting distribution (which is quite independent of where I started). We can imagine a hill of probability piled up somewhere around the E equilibrium point, since any extreme departure from E tends to be pulled back by the internal dampening of the system toward E again.[7]

---

[7] The system $f_i(y_1, y_2)$ will be antidamped if we add a little *temporary* increasing returns to the first equation of (5), in the form say of $+h(y_1-r)^2$. Then we should have to draw Figure 3 showing spirals oscillating *out of* E and approaching a crucial "limit cycle." Now adding a little stochastic disturbance $u_i(t)$ will lead to an ergodic distribution which has its probability spread like a doughnut around the limit cycle.

FREE WILL AND DETERMINISM AGAIN

The contrast between a system which gradually (forgets and) becomes independent of its past (and forgets it) and one which is changed greatly and forever by the slightest disturbance to it has been likened by some philosophers to the contrast between causality and free will. Clerk Maxwell asserted that a belief in free will was like a belief that the universe reacts in a sensitive and even explosive way to minute changes in its initial conditions, while a belief in determinism is like the belief that the development of the system is insensitive (at once or eventually) to transitory changes in initial conditions. From this standpoint, the causal system of Figure 1 and (4) is to be contrasted with the causal system of Figure 2 and (5) and with an exponentially evolving causal system that could be shown in still another figure.

This same distinction can illuminate the difference between probabalistic chance and deterministic causality. The stochastic disturbances $u_i(t)$ might depict the results of coin or dice tossing. The weather seems to be the outcome of a dice game of the gods. But if our knowledge were better, weather might be describable by a causal process. In the same way, if I could toss a nickel carefully in a windless room, controlling precisely the coin's initial position and torques, I might be able to predict whether heads or tails would come up. (Some schoolboys can control card and coin tosses with uncanny precision.) However, as Poincaré and others have pointed out, what makes a roulette wheel a good chance device is a situation where *the most minute change in initial conditions will have discontinuous effects on the outcome.* A fast turn of the wheel of chance is harder to predetermine and predict than a slow one.

We have here, of course, a hierarchy of knowledge and ignorance. What appears to be inexplicable probability and chance at one level may appear as predictable cause and effect at another. Whether there exists in economics and social sciences, as there does in the quantum mechanics of Heisenberg's uncertainty principle, an *irreducible* level of probability ignorance can only be a subject for idle speculation. With better statistical surveys, I expect economists will learn to predict the volume of next year's investment better. With better study of businessmen's psychology, we might further improve our prediction batting average. But whether we can hope to reduce our imprecision gradually to zero is an issue upon which I confess to some skepticism. But my mind is open to new experience.

TELEOLOGY

There is not space left to do justice to my second topic, teleology. Whereas cause and effect seems to run from earlier time to later time, teleology and purpose seem to reverse the direction of time: where my target will be later determines how I must position myself now. Brute Cause and Lady Purpose seem to be quite distinct, and even opposites. But appearances can be deceiving. And often, just as the behavior of light shows both corpuscular and wave properties, so does the waltz of a pendulum show teleology as well as causality.

Let us watch a ball roll down an inclined plane. Newton describes this causally: at each point and velocity, its rates of change of position and velocity are uniquely determined, as by equation (7). We saw that Galileo could describe this behavior by difference equations (6) alone. But Hamilton (and before him, Fermat, Maupertuis, Euler, and Lagrange) can describe the ball's motion thus: It moves with that special velocity which minimizes a certain integral of action, in comparison with any other behavior-pattern which starts and ends at the same points in the same time! Mathematically, the Newton-Galileo causal law

$$\ddot{S} = C, \; S(t) = \tfrac{1}{2} Ct^2$$

is the necessary and sufficient condition for minimizing Hamilton's integral

$$I = \int_{t_0}^{T} (\tfrac{1}{2} \dot{S}^2 + CS) \, dt = \int_{t_0}^{T} L(S,\dot{S}) \, dt$$

(14)

$$= \int_{t_0}^{T} (\text{Kinetic energy} - \text{potential energy}) \, dt,$$

$$S(t_0) = 0, \quad S(T) = \tfrac{1}{2} CT^2$$

I.e.,

$$\int_{t_0}^{T} [\tfrac{1}{2} (Ct)^2 + C\tfrac{1}{2}Ct^2] \, dt < \int_{t_0}^{T} [\tfrac{1}{2} \dot{S}(t)^2 + CS(t)] \, dt$$

for any $S(t)$ path different from Nature's actual path but starting and ending at the same times and places as the actual ball's motion.

Hamilton's Principle is applicable to all conservative mechanical systems and not merely to falling bodies. According to it, Nature is a great Economist, or economizer. Nature acts *as if* she has purpose and aims.

A NEW BIOLOGICAL PRINCIPLE OF "LEAST ACTION"

I should like to point out that the conservative oscillations of Lotka-Volterra's Figure 2, even though they seem to describe the causal struggle for existence, can, in fact, be shown to accomplish the maximization or minimization of a certain integral.[8] This

[8] Volterra has given a quite different minimum formulation of his problem, involving the cumulative number of each species since the beginning of time, $X(t) = \int_0^t N(s)ds$ $\dot{X}=N$; and instead of an integrand of the form $L(N_1,\dot{N}_1)$, his is of the form $L(X_1,X_2,N_1,N_2)$. As far as I know the present formulation is new, but it would not be surprising if its contents have probably been glimpsed by earlier writers.

integral has no physical-energy connotations and can be written in the form

$$I = \int_{t_0}^{T} L(Y_1, \dot{Y}_1) \, dt \,, \qquad Y_1(t_0) = Y_1^0, \quad Y_1(T) = Y_1^T$$

$$(15) \qquad\qquad\qquad\qquad Y_1(t) = \log y_1(t), \quad y_1(t) = e^{Y_1\,(t)}$$

$$L(Y_1, \dot{Y}_1) = \left\{ (a_1 - \dot{Y}_1) \log (a_1 - \dot{Y}_1) - (a_1 - \dot{Y}_1) \right\}$$

$$- \left\{ +a_2 Y_1 - a_{21} e^{Y_1} \right\}$$

$$= T(\dot{Y}_1) - V(Y_1)$$

The conditions sufficient for a minimum of $I, T - t_0$ being not too large, are known to be

$$0 = \frac{d}{dt} \frac{\partial L}{\partial \dot{Y}_1} - \frac{\partial L}{\partial Y_1} \quad, \quad 0 < \frac{\partial^2 L}{\partial \dot{Y}_1{}^2} = T''(\dot{Y}_1)$$

$$(16) \qquad\qquad = \frac{-d}{dt} \log (a_1 - \dot{Y}_1) + a_2 - a_{21} e^{Y_1}$$

$$= \frac{\ddot{Y}_1}{a_1 - \dot{Y}_1} + a_2 - a_{21} e^{Y}$$

or

$$(16)' \qquad\qquad \ddot{Y}_1 = (a_1 - \dot{Y}_1) \, (-a_2 + a_{21} e^{Y_1})$$

But it is easy to convert (5) into this equivalent form. Differentiate the first equation of (5), and then substitute for $\dot{Y}_2$ the expression given for $\dot{Y}_2$ from the second equation, to get

$$\frac{d}{dt}\frac{\dot{y}_1}{y_1} = \ddot{Y}_1 = \frac{d}{dt}(a_1 - a_{21}e^{Y_2}) = -a_{21}e^{Y_2}\dot{Y}_2$$

$$= (a_1 - \dot{Y}_1)\dot{Y}_2 = (a_1 - \dot{Y}_1)(-a_2 + a_{21}e^{Y_1})$$

This shows the equivalence of (16)′ to the Lotka-Volterra causal system (5). Finally, note that $T''(\dot{Y}_1) = -1/(a_1 - \dot{Y}_1) = 1/a_{21}e^{Y_2} > 0$, which is the Legendre condition sufficient for a minimum when $T - t_0$ is sufficiently limited.

MOTHER NATURE'S MYOPIA

One marvels that the causal motion of a pendulum (or deer-man system) actually solves a minimum problem, producing a lower value to Hamilton's integral than any other motion that begins and ends at the same places and at the same times. But closer examination shows that this minimizing holds *only if the time of the motion is shorter than a half-cycle of the pendulum.* (In mathematical terms, there will be a Jacobi "conjugate point" that violates the minimum when the time duration becomes too long.)

Men used to marvel that "Nature abhors a vacuum," until experience with air pressure required the prosaic codicil, "Nature abhors a vacuum only up to 30 inches of mercury." At the least, Mother Nature acts as if she were careless or shortsighted in her mechanics. It is as if I am trying to go from New York to Chicago, and I carefully work out the great-circle route that goes through them. But instead of heading directly west and truly minimizing the distance of travel, I permit myself to head east. Along this round-about path I am forever minimizing the distance between every pair of *nearby* points, but my grand purpose of minimizing distance between New York and Chicago has been thwarted. (Actually, I could have taken any great-circle route going through New York and its antipodal point, and then finished by the unique, direct great-circle route from that antipodal point to Chicago; any of these routes would do as well, or badly, as the unique, indirect great-circle route.

Nature thus seems to favor the motto, "It is better to travel than to arrive." But that is an understatement, for she does travel efficiently for short times. She seems to be a myopic economizer.[9]

This consideration can serve to debunk the mystical notion of teleology introduced by Maupertuis and other eighteenth-century philosophers of nature and deism.

Furthermore, the minute we introduce an iota of friction into the pendulum model, we completely lose the minimum characterization. Adding the viscous-friction term $a\dot{y}$ (or $-a\dot{y}$) to the $\ddot{y} + my = 0$ of (ii) destroys the Euler-Lagrange-Hamilton minimizing.

Similarly, introducing diminishing returns into the Lotka-Volterra system (5) gives us Figure 1's damped notion. And to this causal system, there is no simple teleological counterpart.

---

[9] How short is a short time? In some problems one adds more and more oscillators along a line. In the limit as the number of particles becomes indefinitely large and the intervals between them indefinitely small, we approach the mechanics of a continuous rope or membrane. However, it can be shown that adding each new particle may reduce (even halve) the time before the critical conjugate point comes to destroy the minimum. So when we go to the infinite limit, we are left with no finite time within which the minimum takes place. This explains the paradox that the partial differential equation of the rope or membrane may represent a vanishing of the first variation of a generalized Hamilton integral, but *not* provide any kind of a minimum. Physicists rarely seem to care whether their vanishing first variations represent a true extremum; indeed, one gathers in wave mechanics that the mere presence of a stationary value will lead to observable reinforcements of waves and probabilities. (I do not know whether my suggested instaneous minimum principle will survive through the limit process involved in approaching the continuous rope or membrane.)

A NEW INSTANTANEOUS MINIMUM PRINCIPLE

Some minds boggle at the thought of "action at a distance." Why rely on Nature's having even short-sighted prevision and purpose? Is there not some way of preserving the causality format of the behavior equation—in which the pendulum's acceleration $\ddot{y}$ is related instantaneously to its current position y and velocity $\dot{y}$—while saying that Nature chooses out of all possible accelerations $\ddot{y}$ precisely that critical observed $\ddot{y}^*$ that minimizes some definable magnitude?

I propose to sketch here an affirmative answer to these questions, introducing a limit process into the suggestive Caratheodory method of steepest descent.

This formulation may have some parallel with Gauss's principle of least constraint, which is also an instantaneous minimum principle. But there is no dependence here upon Newtonian laws in Euclidean space, concepts which have no relevance to biological systems (like that of Lotka-Volterra) or to economic systems.[10]

Write the standard integral as a function of its right-hand end point and as a functional of $x(t)$ in the interval

$$(17) \quad I \begin{bmatrix} & t = T \\ T,X: & x(t) \\ & t = t_0 \end{bmatrix} = \int_{t_0}^{T} L \begin{bmatrix} t,x(t),\dot{x}(t) \end{bmatrix} dt \quad \begin{aligned} x(t_0) &= x_0 \\[1em] x(t) &= X \end{aligned}$$

---

[10] The proposed principle has nothing to do with the trivial device by which any law $\ddot{y} = E(y,\dot{y},t)$ is given the minimum formulation $(\ddot{y} - E)^2$ to be a minimum.

Suppose $\partial^2 L/\partial \dot{x}^2 > 0$ everywhere so that I is truly minimized for $T - t_0$ sufficiently small.

Let $x(t) = x(t)^*$ be the minimizing extremal satisfying the Euler condition

$$\frac{d}{dt}\frac{\partial L}{\partial \dot{x}} - \frac{\partial L}{\partial x} = 0, \quad \text{or} \quad \ddot{x}^* = E(t,x,\dot{x})$$

Denote by V

$$V(T,X) = \mathop{I[T,X : x(t)^*]}\limits_{t=t_0}^{t=T}$$

and let $U\ (T,X)$ be the value of I along *any* other path $x(t)$. Now in U and V let the end point X be subject to this same arbitrary path $X(T) = x(T)$, giving

$$U(T,X(T)) = U(T), V(T,X(T)) = V(T)$$

These are parametric equations which define a unique relation, for T-t_0 small and the integrand arranged so that $U'(0) \neq 0$, between U and V, namely

(19) $\qquad U = f(V) = a_0 + a_1 V + a_2 V^2 + a_3 V^3 + R_4$

where the remainder term R_4 involves terms of the fourth degree and higher.

Of course, if the arbitrary path $X(T) = x(T)$ happened to be picked as the extremal path $x(T)^*$, then $f(V) \equiv 1$. By virtue of the Legendre minimum condition, we know that

(20)

$$f(V) > V \quad \text{for } V > 0$$

$$\text{and } x(T) \neq x(T)^*$$

$$f(V) < V \quad \text{for } V < 0$$

This last condition follows from the fact that setting $T < 0$ leads to changing the sign of the integrand in I and to a maximum rather than minimum problem.

Routine (but tedious) calculation shows that

$$a_0 = 0, a_1 = 1, a_2 = 0, a_3 = A[t_0,x(t_0),\dot{x}(t_0),\ddot{x}(t_0)]$$

Indeed, from (20) alone, we could deduce $a_2 = 0$. Furthermore, from the minimum properties of (17) and (20), we can deduce that Nature's choice of $\ddot{x}_0 = E(t_0,x_0,\dot{x}_0)$ does indeed minimize a_3, actually, at zero. Thus, we are led to the following basic theorem

Theorem: If $\ddot{x}^* = E(t,x,\dot{x})$ provides the minimizing solution to

$$I = \int_{t_0}^{T} L(t,x,\dot{x})dt, \qquad \frac{\partial^2 L}{\partial \dot{x}^2} > 0$$

$$x(T) = X, \quad x(t_0) = x_0$$

then it also provides the minimum solution to the scalar problem

(21)
$$\text{Min}_{\{\ddot{x}\}} A(t,x,\dot{x},\ddot{x}) = A(t,x,\dot{x},E(t,x,\dot{x})) = A^* = 0$$

The same holds if x is a vector of functions and whatever the side-conditions on the minimum problem.

To complete the proof of this theorem one need only note that unless $a_3 > 0$, the inequalities of (20) would be violated. And of course $a_3 = 0$ is the condition for the optimizing motion.

RUNNING TIME BACKWARD

If teleology differs from causality by a reversal of time effects, economics can provide numerous interesting examples of the difference, alone with some amusing false examples.

1. One false example would be the fallacy connected with "regression toward the mean." Sir Francis Galton pointed out that the children of very tall (or short) parents tend to be less tall (or short) on the average. From this some inferred wrongly that the race was becoming more homogeneous in height. But actually, in a stationary time series, the parents of very tall children will tend to be less tall—in a perfectly symmetric way, just by virtue of the fact that an imperfect correlation coefficient must be less than 1 in absolute value.

2. In connection with simple Yule-Wold autoregressive schemes, of the type

$$(21) \qquad y(t+1) = ay(t) + u(t) \qquad , \qquad |a| < 1$$

where $u(t)$ is a random shock, we shall observe the serial correlation coefficient $r(y_t, y_{t+1}) < 1$ and with the sign of a. But from the sample of observations alone, can we ever *know* that the system was not generated *teleologically* by

$$(22) \qquad y(t-1) = ay(t) + u(t)$$

If so, is a belief in cause and effect a dogma or convention rather than an empirical inference?

3. If a set of observations, such as data on social classes of fathers, sons, grandsons, . . . is generated by a simple Markov chain, as discussed in an earlier section, no one can stop us from working out for the sample in question the "conditional frequencies" of previous generations. Thus, given that a man is in the upper classes, what fractions of the parents or grandparents of

such a typical man were also U rather than non-U? Interestingly, the resulting two-way conditional frequency would have the Markov-chain property. I.e., knowing what that man's son status was will add no information to help narrow down our prediction as to what status his father had, and so on indefinitely.[11]

4. A simple Keynes multiplier model traces expenditure today to incomes received yesterday, as in

$$Y(t+1) = A\,Y(t) + G(t)$$

where A represents the "marginal propensity to consume" (in simple or in matrix form). For a single impulse of autonomous investment or government expenditure G, or for a repeated plateau, we end up with the convergent multiplier formula

$$(23) \qquad Y = (I + A + A^2 \ldots) \, G = (I - A)^{-1} \, G = MG$$

But exactly the same mathematics of positive A matrixes is

---

[11] A special case is the Ehrenfest win model mentioned earlier. If urn A now has N_t of the 100 balls, the probability that it will next period have $(1 + N_t)$ is $(100 - N_t)/100$ and that it will have $(N_t - 1)$ is $N_t/100$. In a long sample, what is the empirical frequency ratio that it had $(1 + N_t)$ and $(N_t - 1)$ respectively at the *previous* time $t - 1$? The exact result will depend on the *initial* number of balls in urn A, N_0. Or we might stipulate an initial probability for each value of N_0, perhaps giving each N_0 the probability it would have in the ergodic state, which is its average frequency in a very long sample. However, in a long sample of size N, as N goes to infinity, we expect the required empirical frequency ratio to become more and more insensitive to the initial condition; and in many such special cases, the backward or inverse probability matrix will have the same numbers as the original Markov matrix. Thus, if A has no balls now, it must have one ball next period with $P = 1$. But if it has none now, it must, with $P = 1$, have lost one last period. The Ehrenfest schemata to dissolve the paradox of time's asymmetry and increasing entropy seems itself to have the paradox of a time reversibility pattern in its "inverse" Markov matrix. Indeed, it is the stochastic version of Figure 1, with its probability ergodic state created by its dampening, that seems to possess the property of Ehrenfest's interpretation of the Second Law of Thermodynamics. "Increasing entropy" becomes merely "regression toward the mean" in a stationary (not evolving) time series.

involved in a Leontief input-output model. But now inputs are required before outputs, and we write

(24)
$$X(t - 1) = A\,X(t) + G(t)$$
$$X = (I + A + A^2 + \ldots)\,G = MG$$

where now G represents autonomous consumption, and where each of the rounds take place backward in time: one period before G, we need AG; the period before that, to produce AG, we need $A(AG) = A^2G$; and so the multiplier chain goes backward forever in the teleological scenario of preparation for *Der Tag*.

5. In dynamic capital models of the Dorfman-Samuelson-Solow [12] or von Neumann type, often there is a dualism of prices and quantities. If the quantity relations are well behaved backward in time, as in the previous Leontief example, the prices may be well behaved running forward in time; or vice versa.

6. In connection with ideal futures market pricing, the analysis becomes so forward looking as to reek of teleology. As in the famous 1928 Frank Ramsey model of saving, one must know how things work out until the end of time. The problem bristles with paradoxes and divergent integrals; only in certain special cases, can use of "bliss" and "discounting" devices lead to determinate results.

Of course, most paradoxes come from considering idealized models that involve infinity somewhere. Thus, the Ruml Plan introduced during the Second World War, which forgave us one year of taxes permanently but required us to be taxed currently, ends up in an ever-growing economy giving the government more, rather than less money. "To him who forgives, shall be given" is unsound for each closed cycle; but if you pile on more and more incomplete cycles, the absurd becomes sound. I can

[12] R. Dorfman, P. A. Samuelson, R. M. Solow, *Linear Programming and Economic Analysis* (New York: McGraw-Hill, 1958), especially Chapters 9-12. M. Morishima, *Equilibrium Stability and Growth* (Oxford: Oxford University Press, 1964) p. 99 deals with dynamic price behavior, and gives references to 1959 work of Solow.

refer the reader to P. A. Samuelson, "An Exact Consumption-Loan Model of Interest," *Journal of Political Economy*, Vol. 16, No. 6 (1958), pp. 467-82 for more paradoxes created by never-ending exponential growth. Also, "Intertemporal Price Equilibrium," *Weltwirtschaftliches Archiv.*, Vol. 79 (1957), pp. 181-22, for a mixed teleological-causal, speculative-price model which depends, in principle, upon all the harvests that are ever to come. See p. 217, where H_t represents the sequence of harvests; Q_t the sequence of stocks of grain; $C_t = H_t + Q_t - Q_{t+1}$ the sequence of consumptions; $F(C_t) = P_t$, the sequence of market prices; and $T(Q_{t+1}) = P_{t+1} - P_t$, the sequence of Working equilibrium price differences corresponding to each level of stocks that must be carried. This yields the infinite sequence of equations

$$(25) \quad F(H_{t+1} + Q_{t+1} - Q_{t+2}) - F(H_t + Q_t - Q_{t+1}) - T(Q_{t+1}) = 0$$

If we start out with known $(H_0, H_1, \ldots, H_n; Q_0, Q_{n+1}, P_{n+1} = F)$, and write the above equation for $t = 0, 1, \ldots, n-1$, we get a determinate solution for $Q_1, \ldots, Q_n$. The fact that our boundary conditions are two-sided shows that the system is neither time-phased backward in the causal sense nor forward in the teleological sense, but, rather, is time-reversible like the classical pendulum case. Around an equilibrium harvest plateau $H_t \equiv H$, a small transient disturbance can be analyzed by the linear approximation

$$(26) \quad (Q_{t+1} - 2Q_t + Q_{t+1}) + \lambda Q_t = 0$$

where $\lambda = T'(Q^*)/F'(C^*) < 0$. The result is indefinite propagation of the disturbance backward and forward throughout all time. This implies that the linear approximation has to be abandoned and suggests to me that generalized limit cycles of the cobweb type may be involved.

7. I am not sure but that the last phenomenon of indefinite propagation of a disturbance is linked up to the oldest problem

of business-cycle theory. In 1929 we saw a repetition of what has happened often in the last several hundred years: for whatever reason, people begin to think that common stocks or tulips will rise in price; so they buy and hold them, ensuring the rise in $P(t)$ they had expected. If the percentage rise in price, measured by $\dot{P}/P$ or by $[P(t+1) - P(t)]/P(t)$, stays constant, the process could, in principle, go on indefinitely. The rising putative terminal value at some future date justifies present actions.

Now obviously, if in a finite time we have to go through a complete cycle, the stupendous rise in P will be seen to have been mistaken. After the Dutch "Tulip mania" of the seventeenth century was over, people realized that one bulb should not be worth one horse and carriage. But if the time involved were infinite, the absurd exponential solution could formally go on forever!

The important thing for economics is not that market booms will go on forever. The important thing is that economists do not have any good theory of *how long they are likely to go on*. This oldest problem of empirical business cycles may be one of the last we shall be able to give a scientifically valid solution to.

8. Consider the following stochastic process:

$$(27) \quad \begin{bmatrix} a_{11} & a_{12} \\ a_{21} & a_{22} \end{bmatrix} \begin{bmatrix} Ey_1 \\ Ey_2 \end{bmatrix} = \begin{bmatrix} b_{11} & b_{12} \\ b_{21} & b_{22} \end{bmatrix} \begin{bmatrix} y_1 \\ y_2 \end{bmatrix} + \begin{bmatrix} u_1 \\ u_2 \end{bmatrix}$$

where $Ey_i(t)$ is short for $y_i(t+1)$ *and* $E^{-1}y_i(t) = y_i(t-1)$, and the u_i are stochastic disturbances. It can be written in brief matrix terms as

$$(27) \quad AEy = By + U$$

In modern econometrics, we would speak of a case of simple causality if the off-diagonal terms in A were zero: then, with A a "diagonal matrix," each y_i is a simple function of the past variables and the stochastic u_i. We would speak of a "recursive system" if A could be made "triangular," with all the off-diagonal elements above (or below) the diagonal being 0. Finally, we have a "simultaneous" system, if the A matrix (which I assume to be nonsingular, with an existent inverse A^{-1}) cannot be put into triangular form.

But (27) can easily be converted into diagonal-causal form, thus

$$A^{-1} AEy = A^{-1} By + A^{-1} U$$
$$Ey = \tilde{B}y + \tilde{U}$$

where $\tilde{B}$ is the new matrix $A^{-1}B$, and so on. Indeed, if A is nonsingular, we can, in a variety of ways, convert it into triangular form: i.e., there exists a nonsingular matrix S, such that $A^*Ey = B^*y + U^*$, where the triangular matrix $A^* = SA$, and $B^* = SB$ is a new B matrix.

Without the disturbance terms U, these reformulations would be indistinguishable. With the disturbances, they differ in the specified stochastic properties of the U, $\tilde{U}$, U^* disturbances. Thus, suppose an original A is not diagonal or triangular, and the original U are serially uncorrelated random variables independent of any $y_i(t)$. If we convert the system into $(\tilde{A}, \tilde{B}, \tilde{U})$ or (A^*, B^*, U^*) the new U variables will be correlated with each other and with some of the y_i variables. And so, of course, the usual conditions for unbiased least-squares estimation are *not* met.

Now some investigators believe in the dogma that, *if* we could reorganize the right variables, reality is really diagonal-causal with the U disturbances "well-behaved." Others believe that ultimate reality is "really" triangular-recursive with the U disturbances well behaved. Still others, perhaps those connected with the Frisch-Haavelmo Oslo group and the Cowles Foundation, believe the general case is admissible.

I am not sure how a deep issue like this could, in principle, be resolved. Personally, if I had to believe in a dogma, it would be one so general as to degenerate into a convention. I suppose the vector $[y_i(t), u_i(t)]$ would be a nonlinear functional, as is (1)′, of the past time-profiles of all variables. Since the stochastic variables are themselves determinately "explained" at their own level, there is nothing involved in putting the system into diagonal-causal form. Indeed, as in physics, we may always work with generalized coordinates, which are related by nonsingular, not necessarily linear transformations to (y_i, u_i). What a miracle that the coordinate we happen to use or observe should be truly in triangular or diagonal form!

As soon as we recognize that all systems like (27) are idealizations, we are at liberty to assume the most general form for A, raising all the difficult problems of simultaneous-equation estimation. As a familiar illustration of this, let me mention a theorem that I stumbled on years ago.

Suppose A is truly diagonal (or triangular), with well-behaved independent U's. But suppose, instead of observing each $y_i(t)$, we observe the nonoverlapping totals $y_i(t + 1) + y_i(t + 2) + \ldots + y_i(t + N) = Z_i(T)$ where $Z_i(T)$ is defined only for $T = Nt$ integral values. Then, in a stationary time series as N becomes large, Z_i becomes more and more a constant. To avoid disappearance of variance, let us change each u_i to $f(N)u_i$, where $f(N)$ is an appropriate increasing function of N.

Now let us put the $Z_i(T)$ observed variables into the form

$$(28) \qquad A_N Z(T+N) = B_N Z(T) + U_N(T)$$

The theorem says that the best choice of A_N will almost certainly *not* be diagonal or triangular but will require simultaneous-equation estimation procedures.

The implications are far-reaching and not particularly favorable to ordinary least-squares. If true causality takes place at the microsecond level, but our observations involve months or years (and they must involve such long periods if uninteresting "error" is to be cancelled out), then we cannot expect triangular-recursive least-squares methods to be useful very often. (One way of looking at "controlled experimentation" is that it may give truly diagonal-causal estimation models.)

PSEUDO-TELEOLOGY

I shall conclude with some examples in economics and other sciences that are couched in terms of teleology and purpose but which can be found to be essentially free of true teleology. Or, to put the matter in a different way, important aspects of what we ordinarily call teleology can be related to certain aspects of causality.

1. Economists deal with maximum systems, and these behave in definite ways. After you have dealt with such systems for a long time, you may fall into the natural anthropomorphic habit of imputing "will" and "volition" to them. This is perhaps only a figure of speech; but often it is a useful one, for the maximum systems do react to certain disturbances *as if* they were reasoning beings.

For example, a rope will hang in the shape of a catenary if suspended freely between two points that are closer together than its length. Why? Because a catenary is the shape that leads to the lowest center of gravity of the rope. And just as an olive, subject to a little friction, will run down the cocktail glass to its bottom, where the olive's center of gravity is at a minimum, so the rope "tries" to achieve the lowest center of gravity. (Both olive and rope are subject to purely causal laws of swing; but friction slows them down according to causal laws and they can come to rest only where the center of gravity is at a minimum.) Suppose I nail down a midpoint of the rope to an arbitrary point: now the rope will readjust and hang in catenaries for each of the segments, acting as if it knows it has a rendezvous to minimize (subject to the new constraint) its center of gravity.

We need not stick to ropes, olives, and soap bubbles. If farmers are maximizing profits, they will react to the reduction in the price of fertilizer by using more of it. What is surprising about that? As profit maximizers they are teleologists. But consider all the independent farmers in a county or region. Add their fertilizer purchases together and study how this total reacts to a lowering of the price of fertilizer. It acts qualitatively the same as any one farm's purchase does. And yet there is no trade association for the whole county, which has a mind and which uses that mind to maximize the profits of the group. Still, and this is the point, the observing economist can set up the fictional hypothesis that there is such a maximizing mind, and often he can make fruitful predictions from it.

When we come to certain other aspects, like the LeChatelier Principle (which is treated in my cited *Foundations*, Chapter 3), it is even more uncanny how detailed will be the predicted reactions of a maximum system, just as if it were exercising intelligence.

2. Thus far, I have been describing positive facts about economic behavior. Now turn to the problem of *welfare economics* —how a system ought normatively to behave. Adam Smith was one of the first, but certainly not the last, to speak as if within the impersonal market place of perfect competition there was a magical "invisible hand" leading the system to a certain kind of optimum—even though each individual is merely pursuing his own selfish well-being. Smith could not state the principle correctly, nor could anyone before this century. But modern economists know that there is a germ of truth (along with a virus of falsehood) in this theorem. Of course, there is no invisible hand. But it is true that the conditions of perfect competition lead to equations—just as the dying out of rope swings lead to catenary equations—which have certain *efficiency* properties. As a result, in my technical work in mathematical economics, I often reduce my equations down to those of such a maximum system and then reason correctly from the obvious properties of a maximizer. The point is that this normative approach leads to correct positive descriptions about the resulting observable equations.

3. Biology provides even better examples of teleology or pseudo-teleology. We say that the function of the kidney is to purify the

blood—as if some watchmaker had designed it, or as if the kidney were an alert sentry knowing its job. Actually, there are only cause and effect relations of osmotic pressure going on in the kidney. But the biologist has learned heuristically that he can often shortcircuit his description by speaking in the parable language of teleology.

4. Even without any original far-sighted designer, a world that involves struggle for survival may evolve in such a way as to appear to have certain maximizing properties. In economics, Armen Alchian of UCLA[13] has pioneered in pointing out how mere survival of competitors may lead to persistence of those units which act as if they were maximizing, whether or not everybody or anybody is really maximizing. But earlier, such biologists as L. J. Henderson, the ancient Greeks, and many Darwinians already had an inkling that "stable forms tend to persist." Henderson even wrote a seminal book entitled *The Fitness of the Environment,* in which he pointed out how unusual were the conditions on this planet and how appropriate they were to support life as we know it. Had he lived on another kind of planet, he would have had to write another kind of a book, and on lifeless planets no books get written.

I suppose the most striking version of this kind of teleology in biology is to be found in the classic writing by Walter Cannon on *The Wisdom of the Body.* Although the usual laws of physics, and particularly of negative feedback circuits, are all that are involved in most physiological processes, one gets a shorthand description of actual behavior by using the image and terminology of purpose and teleology. Only after one realizes that this is merely a figure of speech should one be permitted to use the figure of speech—just as we should only permit those people to continue to smoke who are able to break themselves of the habit.

5. There are numerous examples in economics of the negative feedback concept which is so dear to the hearts of modern electrical and systems engineers. Thus, suppose people spend ⅔ of their incomes on consumption and save or invest the remaining

[13] Armen A. Alchian, "Uncertainty, Evolution, and Economic Theory," *Journal of Political Economy,* LVIII (June, 1950), 211-21.

⅓. Then if new investment spending of a billion dollars comes along, economists say loosely, "National income must go up by 3 times the increment of investment, because no other multiplier would cause income to grow enough to create the new saving needed to finance the investment." Actually, that is precisely what will happen in simple models but it does not happen because the system or anybody in it knows that it has a rendezvous with this new equilibrium level. It happens because the sum of the billion dollar investment spending plus ⅔ of that amount plus ⅔ of ⅔ of that amount . . . leads ultimately to a total of 3 times that amount, by virtue of the algebraic identity]

$$[1 + \tfrac{2}{3} + (\tfrac{2}{3})^2 + \cdots + (\tfrac{2}{3})^n + \cdots] = 1/(1 - \tfrac{2}{3}) = 3.$$

I do not think that this interplay between ideas in economics and in biology is accidental. I would remind you that not only was Charles Darwin led (as he has told us) to his theory of evolution by thinking about the economic population theories of Malthus but also Alfred Wallace, the independent discoverer of evolution, was led (as he has told us) to the theory by thinking about the work of Malthus.

6. Even in physics, if one takes the prosaic view of Mach, one may be able to reduce the statement that light travels between two points in a straight line to the Darwin-Huygens formulation that, although light raylets travel in every direction at every point, the fastest arrivers are those survivors who have drunkenly straggled in the straight-line path and not been cancelled out by interference patterns. This adds a new duality to my earlier duality of causality and teleology, namely a duality of wave and particle in nonquantum mechanics phenomena.

Let me conclude with the remark that my resolution to stick primarily to economics got violated as I became carried away by my subject. I would have stuck to this subject that many people unaccountably think dull, but, like Dr. Samuel Johnson's schoolmate who had hoped to become a philosopher, I was thrown off my purpose as cheerfulness kept randomly breaking in.

Noncausal Explanation

ABRAHAM KAPLAN

THE importance for methodology of the concept of causality has been grossly exaggerated for many decades. Although philosophers have been widely aware of this exaggeration, in proportion to their recognition of the role of mathematics in science, many scientists, especially those who do not make much use of mathematics, still talk as though their central aim is to arrive at causal explanations of the phenomena they study. I want to redirect attention, therefore, to the methodological legitimacy and scientific value of non-causal explanations.

The heyday of causal explanation occurred about a century ago. It was marked by the insistence on mechanical models as not just ideal explanations but as the only models that really explain. Causal connection was thought to be paradigmatically illustrated by the impact of one billiard ball on another, and causal chains by a falling row of dominoes. One event causes another in the way in which the movement of one body brings it about that another body moves in a certain way.

There was a time when models of this kind did justice to the major scientific achievements of the period, though never to all of them, by any means. In any case, that time is long past. In these matters there is inevitably a certain cultural lag: methodological thinking in behavioral science suffers, I think, not from imitating physics but from imitating what physics is mistakenly thought to be—what it certainly is not now and perhaps never was.

A number of philosophers have recently been concerned with arriving at an exact formulation of causal connection. Some scientists and logicians have expressed strong doubts whether this can, in principle, be given. To deny the possibility in principle may be going too far, but it is surely true that there are serious difficulties to be overcome. What is meant by saying that one thing

145

causes another is by no means intuitively clear, and more exact re-statements cannot easily be shown to have the content we might intuitively expect of them. It is one thing to satisfy the conditions laid down by the analyst of the concept, and quite another to satisfy the requirements for the usefulness of the concept imposed by scientific inquiry itself.

Causal connection is usually analyzed in terms of some sort of relation of implication: the grammar of the "if-then" conjunction is at least a starting point. If the cause occurs, then its effects occur. Other conditions might then be added, for instance, that the relation be asymmetrical: if A is the cause of B, then B cannot also be the cause of A. And we may also want to say that B occurs only if A occurs (denial of plurality of causes); and so on.

A particularly interesting condition that might be imposed is that of continuity, or at least what mathematicians call "density". between any two elements of the series there is always another. (Consider the fractions ordered by size: although between any two fractions there is another, the series has gaps at the points corresponding to the irrational numbers.) The idea is that if A is the cause of B then there must be an event E such that A causes E and E in turn causes B. But then there must be another event E' such as that A causes E' and E' causes E, and another event E'' caused by E and in turn causing B; and so on indefinitely.

The significance of this condition of density is that it turns the interest in causal explanation in the direction of microtheories. For intermediate events are progressively more limited in space and time, and as more and more intermediates are identified the causal connection is more and more fully specified. But, by the same token, where inquiry does not give microtheories a preferred status, causal explanation is correspondingly irrelevant. I would not wish to say that something has been explained only when we have traced the microconnections with their antecedents, or even only when we can believe that such connections exist (gravitation explains planetary motions even if it is regarded as "action at a distance").

The view I want to take is that causality is significant in the philosophy of science chiefly when science is seen as an instrument of control over phenomena. Causality is introduced just insofar as we are concerned with the effects of the intervention of the investigator. The concept of causality belongs not to the subject matter, independent of the inquirer's perspective, but to the concept of the subject matter that is related to a particular perspective of the inquirer. This is his being able to intervene in the conditions that he has studied—perhaps in that controlled intervention that we call experiment. Without giving any direct arguments in behalf of this view, I want to go on to some alternatives to the causal conception to se what can be made of them, especially in the understanding of the behavioral sciences.

The centrality of the notion of control (or intervention) in relation to causality is revealed by the fundamental distinction between so-called causes and conditions. It is impossible to make sense of this distinction except by reference to the possibility, or desirability, of intervention by the experimenter (or, in general, the observer).

The emphasis on the centrality of causal connections is one every scientist would have to accept, if construed as it was in the philosophic tradition, as a kind of heuristic principle. In the form given by Leibniz in the nineteenth century it is the principle of sufficient reason: nothing happens unless there is a good reason for it to happen. In these terms I have no objections to the principle of causality, except that I would still caution against our introducing as necessary conditions for intelligibility (or for explanatory force) certain special features that attach to causal laws in the particular and narrow sense in which these can be distinguished from scientific laws in general.

That is, if the notion of causality is applied so widely that it is equated with intelligibility (or with what is explicable) I would go along with it, because I believe that, in principle, nothing lies outside the realm of intelligibility (the realm of what is explicable). But if causality were adduced as a particular principle among other possibilities for intelligibility—or for demarcating the realm of what is explicable—then I would repudiate it as the sole principle, and emphasize other ways for making things intelligible or providing explanations. This is what I shall now discuss.

I shall begin with some intermediate types of explanation that are not causal but are clearly explanatory.

First, many explanatory principles in the behavioral sciences are essentially taxonomic. I believe that taxonomic principles are indeed explanatory, but I feel that they are weakly so. Something is gained when we place phenomena within a taxonomic scheme, although how much depends upon the merits of the taxonomic scheme as a whole. Even a very good taxonomic scheme is radically different from a causal one, for taxonomy does not tell us what the causes are. We might suppose that the merits of the taxonomy depend upon how cleanly and neatly it can be related to causal principles. But that is an open question, and scientists can agree on the scientific usefulness of a taxonomy even when they disagree about the causal laws that are going to be formulated in terms of it, and even when they cannot formulate causal laws.

Second, there are certain generalizations—in the natural sciences they are by far the largest class, perhaps even the whole—that are not causal because they formulate mathematical relationships. In most laws in the natural sciences, or at any rate a very great many of them, one magnitude is formulated as a mathematical function of certain other magnitudes, and the content of the law is to this effect: given a set of variables, if values are specified for certain of them, then mathematical relationships determine the values, or at least the range of values, to be assigned to the other variables related to those given. These are distinctively not causal relationships, for two reasons. First, they do not involve the kind of implication of intermediates that a causal relationship does. When I say that A causes B, I imply that insofar as it is possible for us to identify an intervening condition, say B', my assertion is to be understood as implying that A causes B' and B' causes B. And if we are able to identify still other intermediates, then my assertion also is to be understood as implying that A causes these intermediates which in turn cause B', which in turn causes B, and so on, as far as the intermediates can be identified.

No such implications are to be taken as involved in the statement of the mathematical relationship. Secondly, the mathematical relationship differs from the causal because the causal implies a temporal order. In the usual sense of the term, if we say that A causes B, we mean it in such a way that it would be wrong to say, "And moreover B causes A." There are, of course, many causal cycles that we might loosely describe in this way. For instance, in the simplest kind of electric buzzer, closing the circuit causes the iron core of the electrical coil to become magnetized, which causes the spring-arm of the buzzer to be pulled toward one pole of the magnet, which causes the circuit to be broken, which causes the core to be no longer magnetized, which causes the spring arm to fly back, which causes it to close the circuit, and so on. But obviously here it is not that A causes B and B causes A. It is that A causes an event of the kind B, let us say $B1$, and then $B1$ causes another event of the kind A, say $A2$, which in turn causes an event of the kind B, say $B2$, and so on. There is no strict symmetry but only a recurrence of a pattern of asymmetrical relations. I say that the mathematical relationships differ from the causal ones in not making implications about intermediates and in not having the asymmetry required for a causal connection.

A third kind of noncausal explanatory principle is the statistical. The statistical principle comes closer to the causal in that it is not necessarily subject to the symmetry characteristic of the mathematical laws that apply in the nonstatistical branches of natural science. If I may simplify, the laws of mechanics are symmetrical and therefore cannot be construed as causal laws, in spite of the fact that our usual images of causal connections are those derived from mechanics. There is a kind of irony in this. If we ask people to abandon their philosophical preconceptions, what do they really mean by a causal connection? The chances are that they will invoke images from those fields of physics in which causality has the least important role, because there, everything that they refer to is completely symmetrical. If a movie of a game of billiards showed only the motion of the billiard balls, it would be impossible to decide whether it was being run forward or backward. In order to make that decision we would need to observe something like the cigarette that is being smoked by one of the billiard players. Then we could very safely infer that if in one of the frames the ash is still on the cigarette, and if in another frame the ash is scattered on the floor, the events occurred in that order. It could not be that ash was scattered and some time afterwards rose from the floor and converged at the tip of the cigarette. But in making use of this plausible assumption we would be relying upon aspects of physical theory other than mechanics; in particular we would be relying upon thermodynamics, and similar fields.

Statistical explanation is other than causal because, although it introduces the asymmetry that causality allows for, it lacks the determinism essential to causality.

I confess to a prejudice with regard to statistical explanation. I feel that only a statistical explanation makes sense. A particular case illustrates my feeling.

A familiar law of thermodynamics holds that when one of two adjacent bodies has a much higher temperature than the other, heat will flow from the hot body to the cold. This can be baffling. Why should the flow of heat from the hot body be affected by what is going on around it? Does the hot body say to itself, "What shall I do with all of this heat? Aha, there is a cold body in my environment. Good, I'll pour the heat out."? How does that hot body know that there are cold bodies around it? And knowing that there are cold bodies around it, what is the remarkable mechanism by which it always makes the appropriate decision? This is one of the mysteries that causality tends to gloss over. Why should not the hot body decide: "This time, even though there is a cold body I am going to act as though it were a hot one. We only live once. I have been reading existentialists and thermodynamicists, and this is my last chance." It never happens.

I think that this difficulty can be set aside, and I put it in this way: The hot body behaves just as it does *regardless of what is around it.* If there are other bodies in its neighborhood that are also very warm, they also will behave as they always behave and so they will be radiating heat, a certain amount of which will be absorbed by our hero. As a result, our hero will not cool off as quickly. For, although it radiates heat as fast as it might under any other condition, in the presence of hot bodies it will also absorb a certain amount of heat, and the net effect is that it is not radiating as fast as it otherwise would. This is not because it is taking account of what is in its environment. But because we take environment into account, we assign it causal agency.

The usual view is that statistics gives us a practical approach to matters, but if we really want to understand "how come," we should look at a mechanical, which is to say a causal, explanation. Since each of us has his prejudices, I opt for the prejudice that causal or mechanical regularities are impossible to understand until they are seen as the mass effect of random statistical processes.

There is a fourth kind of subsidiary noncausal explanation, temporal laws, that is, laws in whose formulation the time variable is important. There is a variety of laws of this kind. First are interval laws, which take a form such as this: If something happens at the time $T1$, something else happens at the time $T1$ plus delta, where delta has a definite finite value. We may not be able to say what happens from the time $T1$ to the time $T1$ plus epsilon; where epsilon converges toward zero, but we can say what will happen at $T1$ plus delta, provided that delta has at least such and such a magnitude.

For example, a child psychologist might be willing to say: "If you do the following to this child at such and such a time, then next week or next month or next year or in 20 years this child will exhibit behavior of roughly such and such a kind." But if you were to say to him: "Yes, but what I want to know is: are you prepared to say anything about what will happen to that child a tenth of a second later?" The child psychologist will say, "That is an interesting question, but how am I to know? Am I a neurologist or a neurophysiologist? All I can tell you is that children that are treated in such and such a way in infancy are likely to behave in such and such a way in puberty. My contention is that if what the psychologist says is true or suggestive of further inquiry it deserves to be taken seriously scientifically. It is absurd to suppose that we cannot take it scientifically unless and until the psychologist is prepared to make a commitment with regard to the intervening stages.

There are other kinds of temporal laws. Genetic laws have to do not with just an interval but with an interval related to an appropriate zero point. No child psychologist would answer questions about a child's behavior unless we told him the child's age. A three-year-old will behave very differently from a seven-year-old, very differently from a thirteen-year-old, and so on. It is not just a matter of the length of the interval. The interval between ages seven and twenty is radically different from the interval between birth and thirteen. Genetic laws refer to intervals related to some starting point. Philosophers sometimes formulate other temporal laws that I call pattern laws. These are like genetic laws except that they have a *relative* zero point, referring to the "age" the organization, or the culture, or whatever it may be—that is, its stage in a pattern of development.

In short, in addition to mathematical laws, taxonomic laws, and statistical laws there are temporal laws, with explanatory force, which are also noncausal.

There is still another kind of law, not causal, not taxonomic, not mathematical (that is, not functional in the mathematical sense), not statistical, not temporal, and yet explanatory, that I believe to be the most fundamental to the behavioral sciences. To use the most familiar colloquial terms for it, I call this kind purposive. I want to claim, first, that purposive explanations are not causal explanations (although I do not mean that causal explanations cannot be given for the operation of purposes) and, second, that they are indeed explanatory.

The fact that a causal explanation can be given for the operation of purposes does not mean that a purposive explanation is the same as a causal one. I may ask why a person is doing such and such a thing, and somebody might say that he is doing it because his nervous system is in a certain state of excitation and there are laws to the effect that when the system is in such a state, that action results. This I would call a causal explanation. It would be quite another thing to say that the person is doing something because a pretty girl came into the room, or because his mother had looked at him and said, "Sammy, is that nice after all I've done for you?" or because somebody said to him, "All right, you won't get your Ph.D." I would insist that these latter accounts are also explanatory and that they are sufficiently different from the first one to warrant our methodological recognition of the difference even though we are prepared subsequently to introduce causal explanations. My allowing for the possibility of introducing causal explanations is not to be misconstrued as a secret admission that I feel that we must introduce them ultimately, and that if we do not, the others are not really explanatory.

Scientific methodology suffers very seriously from cultural lag, and a good part of the scientific methodology that is in our minds now was really developed about 50 to 75 years ago; those who developed it were looking at the science 50 to 75 years before that, so that their methodological principles related to the struggle of science for several centuries to free itself from the domination of final causes and to replace them by efficient causes. But in looking at this kind of methodology today I have the same kind of reaction that I have when I read Bernard Shaw or John Galsworthy or other such advanced thinkers of 1910. Although I like to feel that I am an advanced thinker too, I also like to think that I am sufficiently a child of the late twentieth century to recognize that a lot of the things that they were fighting against were not so bad. In the nineteenth century the issue was one of mechanism versus teleology. On one side were idealists and vitalists and the like; on the other side were materialists and mechanists. What I deplore is that so much of twentieth century philosophy has taken a side in the argument whereas I find both sides equally embarrassing. I have as many apologies to offer for the mechanistic materialists as I do for the vitalists and idealists—perhaps even more.

I would urge that our twentieth-century methodology should not be misled by this outmoded issue; the advances within science itself have made it passé. I have in mind especially the advances in cybernetics and related disciplines. The kinds of phenomena that vitalists and teleologists are emphasizing are indeed important, but they can, we now have good reason to think, be analyzed within a framework that satisfies the stringent conditions that the mechanists and causalists laid down. If that is so, we no longer have to worry whether we are satisfying those conditions initially. We can go on about our business and say that anybody whose scientific conscience bothers him is welcome to explore those areas of science that are concerned with bringing the teleological phenomena into relation with the so-called mechanistic phenomena. In any case the teleological phenomena themselves can be adduced in such a way as to have explanatory force.

This can be done in two ways: I call one functional and the other motivational. We are giving a functional explanation when we explain a certain phenomenon by calling attention to the purposes that are served by that phenomenon within a larger, purposive framework. The serious objections to the functional kind of explanation fundamentally are two.

The first objection is that we introduce functional explanations without first having satisfied the condition that there *are* purposive systems operative. The fallacy that this involves may be called the utilitarian fallacy. It amounts to the supposition that we have to explain everything in human affairs by reference to some function that things perform. This may be an unwarranted assumption. It may be that no function is performed; it may be that there once was a situation in which the function was performed but no longer; it may even be that there never was a function performed. It is not that functional explanations are not explanations at all. It is just that when one makes a functional explanation he must be prepared to back it up. He is signing a check for a rather large amount, and unless he can show that he has those funds on deposit he cannot blame anybody for not wanting to negotiate the check.

The second objection is that functional explanations are often formulated in the idiom of motivational explanation. A motivational explanation differs from a functional explanation in that the purpose is entertained. It is not only an end but an end in view. When we say that somebody is doing something on purpose, the expression "on purpose" may mean that a function is being *deliberately* performed. Bees do a great many things on purpose but they have no motives. The second objection to the functional explanation is that we use a motivational idiom in places where, even though the functional idiom is justified, the motivational one certainly is not.

An example is provided by the theory of evolution, which is often said to have replaced final causation with efficient causation. But the phrase "natural selection" belongs to the language of finality, as though there is a Mother Nature who has ends in view. I am afraid that social scientists sometimes take such metaphors literally, and this is certainly objectionable. But sometimes it is literally true that motives are at work, and in those cases references to the motives are genuinely explanatory.

Causal Ordering
and Identifiability * 1

HERBERT A. SIMON

1. INTRODUCTION

IN careful discussions of scientific methodology, particularly those carried on within a positivist or operationalist framework, it is now customary to avoid any use of the notion of causation and to speak instead of "functional relations" and "interdependence" among variables. This avoidance is derived, no doubt, from the role that the concept of causality has played in the history of philosophy since Aristotle, and particularly from the objectionable ontological and epistemological overtones that have attached themselves to the causal concept over the course of that history.

Empiricism has accepted Hume's critique that necessary connections among events cannot be perceived (and hence can have no empirical basis). Observation reveals only recurring associations. The proposition that it is possible to discover associations among events that are, in fact, invariable ceases to be a provable statement about the natural world and becomes instead a working rule to guide the activity of the scientist. He says, "I will seek for relationships among events that seem always to hold in fact, and when it occurs that they do not hold, I will search for additional conditions and a broader model that will (until new exceptions are discovered) restore my power of prediction." The only

° From W. C. Hood and T. C. Koopmans, eds., *Studies in Econometric Method* (John Wiley & Sons, 1953).
¹ I am indebted to Tjalling C. Koopmans for his valuable suggestions and comments on earlier drafts of this chapter, particularly with regard to the discussion of the relation between causal ordering and identifiability. A distinction between endogenous and exogenous variables similar to the concept of causal ordering here developed was made by Orcutt [1952]. For a discussion of the incorporation of the notion of causality in a system of formal logic, see Simon [1952].

"necessary" relationships among variables are the relationships of logical necessity that hold in the scientist's model of the world, and there is no guarantee that this model will continue to describe the world that is perceived.

Even this narrower notion of causality—that causal orderings are simply properties of the scientist's model, properties that are subject to change as the model is altered to fit new observations— has been subjected to criticism on two scores. First of all, the viewpoint is becoming more and more prevalent that the appropriate scientific model of the world is not a deterministic model but a probabilistic one. In quantum mechanics and thermodynamics, and in many social science models, expressions in terms of probabilities have taken the place of completely deterministic differential equations in the relationships connecting the variables. However, if we adopt this viewpoint, we can replace the causal ordering of the variables in the deterministic model by the assumption that the realized values of certain variables at one point or period in time determine the probability distribution of certain variables at later points or periods.

The second criticism is in one sense modest; in another, more sweeping. It has already been alluded to above. It is simply that "causation" says nothing more than "functional relationship" or "interdependence," and that, since "causation" has become encrusted with the barnacles of nonoperationalist philosophy, it is best to abandon this term for the others.

In view of the generally unsavory epistemological status of the notion of causality, it is somewhat surprising to find the term in rather common use in scientific writing (when the scientist is writing about his science, not about its methodology). Moreover, it is not easy to explain this usage as metaphorical, or even as a carryover of outmoded language habits. For, in ordinary speech and writing the causal relationship is conceived to be an asymmetrical one—an ordering—while "functional relationship" and "interdependence" are generally conceived as entirely symmetrical. When we say that A causes B, we do not say that B causes A; but when we say that A and B are functionally related (or interdependent), we can equally say that B and A are functionally related (or interdependent). Even when we say that *A* is the independent variable in an equation, while *B* is the dependent variable, it is often our feeling that we are merely stating a convention of notation and that, by rewriting our equation, we could with equal propriety reverse the roles of *A* and *B*.

The question, then, of whether we wish to retain the word "cause" in the vocabulary of science may be narrowed down to the question of whether there is any meaning in the assertion that the relationship between two variables in a model is sometimes asymmetrical rather than symmetrical. If the answer to this question is in the negative, there would seem to be good reason for abandoning "cause" in favor of its synonyms. If the answer is affirmative, the term "cause," carefully scrubbed free of any undesirable philosophical adhesions, can perform a useful function and should be retained.

It is the aim of this paper to show how the question just raised can be answered in the affirmative and to provide a clear and rigorous basis for determining when a causal ordering can be said to hold between two variables or groups of variables in a model. Two preliminary remarks may help to clarify the approach that will be taken.

First, the concepts to be defined all refer to a model—a system of equations—and not to the "real" world the model purports to describe. Hence both Hume's critique and the determinism-indeterminism controversy are irrelevant to the question of whether these concepts are admissible in scientific discourse. The most orthodox of empiricists and antideterminists can use the term "cause," as we shall define it, with a clear conscience.

Second, it might be supposed that cause could be defined as functional relationship in conjunction with sequence in time. That is, we might say that if *A* and *B* are functionally related and if *A* precedes *B* in time, then *A* causes *B*. There is no logical obstacle to this procedure. Nevertheless, we shall not adopt it. We shall argue that time sequence does, indeed, sometimes provide a basis for asymmetry between *A* and *B*, but that the asymmetry is the important thing, not the sequence. By putting asymmetry, without necessarily implying a time sequence, at the basis of our definition we shall admit causal orderings where no time sequence appears (and sometimes exclude them even when there is a time sequence). By so doing we shall find ourselves in closer accord with actual usage, and with a better understanding of the meaning of the concept than if we had adopted the other, and easier, course. We shall discover that causation (as we shall define it) does not imply time sequence, nor does time sequence imply causation.

We conclude these introductory comments with two examples of relationships that "common sense" would regard as causal. First, the classical work of the biologists Henderson, Cannon, and others on homeostasis is replete with references to asymmetrical relationships among the variables. On thirst, Cannon [1939, pp. 62-66] states: "Thirst is a sensation referred to the inner surface of the mouth and throat, especially to the root of the tongue and the back part of the palate. . . . When water is lacking in the body the salivary glands are unfavorably affected . . . [They] are therefore unable to secrete, the mouth and pharynx become dry and thus the sensation of thirst arises."

The causal chain clearly implied by this statement is

deficiency of water in body tissues→reduction in salivation→dryness of tongue and palate→stimulation of nervous system (sensation of thirst).

To this Cannon adds elsewhere:

→activity of drinking→restoration of water control of tissues.

It is difficult to think or write of these functional relationships as symmetrical, or as asymmetrical but running in the opposite direction. For example, if there is normal salivation but the saliva is prevented from reaching the tongue and palate, thirst is produced, but this neither reduces salivation nor produces a deficiency of water in the body tissues.

Similarly, in economics we speak of relations like

poor growing weather→small wheat crops→increase in price of wheat

and we reject the notion that by changing the price of wheat we can affect the weather. The weather is an "exogenous" variable, the price of wheat an "endogenous" variable.

2. SELF-CONTAINED STRUCTURES

The task we have set ourselves is to show that, given a system of equations and a set of variables appearing in these equations, we can introduce an asymmetrical relationship among individual equations and variables (or subsets of equations and variables) that corresponds to our common-sense notion of a causal ordering. Let us designate the relationship by an arrow, →. Then we shall want to construct our definition in such a manner that $A{\rightarrow}B$ if and only A is a direct cause (in ordinary usage of the term) of B.

In the following discussion we shall seek mathematical simplicity by limiting ourselves to systems of linear algebraic equations without random disturbances. Later we shall indicate how the concepts can readily be extended to nonlinear systems, but a discussion of stochastic systems is beyond the scope of this chapter.

DEFINITION 2.1: A linear structure *is a system of linear nonhomogeneous equations* (cf. Marschak [1950, p. 8]) *that possesses the following special properties:*

(a) *That in any subset of k equations taken from the linear structure at least k different variables appear with nonzero coefficients in one or more of the equations of the subset.*

(b) *That in any subset of k equations in which $m \geqslant k$ variables appear with nonzero coefficients, if the values of any $(m - k)$ variables are chosen arbitrarily, then the equations can be solved for unique values of the remaining k variables.*

In particular, a linear structure is an independent and consistent set of nonlinear nonhomogenous equations, independence and consistency being guaranteed by properties (a) and (b).[2]

DEFINITION 2.2: *A linear structure is* self-contained *if it has exactly as many equations as variables* (cf. Marschak [1950, p. 7]).

Because of (b), a self-contained linear structure possesses a unique solution—there is precisely one set of values of the variables that satisfies the equations.

A linear structure can be represented by the matrix of the coefficients (augmented to include the constant terms) of the equations of the structure. We have already required that the system be nonhomogeneous (that not all the constant terms be zero) and that a sufficient number of variables appear with nonzero coefficients in one or more of the equations in any subset of the structure.

DEFINITION 2.3: *A* linear model *is the class of all linear structures that can be obtained from a given structure by the substitution of new nonzero coefficients for the nonzero coefficients of the original structure* [*without, of course, violating* (a) *or* (b)].[3]

With these terms defined we can undertake to introduce the notion of a causal ordering of the variables, and a corresponding precedence ordering of the equations, of a self-contained linear structure. We shall then see at once that all the linear structures belonging to the same linear model possess the same causal order-

[2] It should be noted that Conditions (a) and (b), incorporated in Definition 2.1, are absent from the definitions of linear structure employed in other chapters. This slight difference in definition simplifies the exposition and should cause the reader little difficulty. The relevant theorems on independence and consistency will be found in Bôcher [1907, pp. 43-49]. Condition (b) can be omitted if we exclude from consideration certain exceptional sets of values of the coefficients of the equation system; in this case we can develop properties of the system, parallel to those described in the present chapter, which hold "almost everywhere" (see Koopmans, Rubin, and Leipnik [1950, p. 82]) in the space of these coefficients.

[3] This definition, for purposes of simplification, is rather narrow.

ing. Hence, we shall see that the causal ordering is determined as soon as we know which variables appear with nonzero coefficients in which equations.

3. CAUSAL ORDERING

3.1. Considering any subset A of the equations of a linear structure (alternatively, a subset of the rows of the augmented coefficient matrix) and the corresponding subset α of the variables that appear with a nonzero coefficient in at least one of the equations of A. Let N_A be the number of equations in A, and n_α the number of variables in α. By (a), $n_\alpha \geqslant N_A$. If we extend Definition 2.2 to subsets of equations in a linear structure, then we may say:

DEFINITION 3.1: *A subset A of a linear structure is* self-contained *if and only if* $n_\alpha = N_A$.

DEFINITION 3.2: *If* $n_\alpha > N_A$ *we shall say that A is* sectional [Marschak, 1950, p. 7].

Now suppose that A and B are two subsets of equations of the same linear structure. We prove the theorem:

THEOREM 3.1: *Let A be self-contained and B be self-contained. Then their intersection C (the set of equations belonging to both A and B) is self-contained.*

Designate by α the set of variables that appear in A, by β the set in B, and by γ the set in C; let $A \cap B$ designate the intersection of the sets A and B, and $A \cup B$ their sum (i.e., the set of elements belonging either to A or to B). Then the theorem states that if $n_a = N_A$, $n_\beta = N_B$, and $C = A \cap B$, then $n_\gamma = N_C$.

PROOF: Designate by N_S the number of equations in $(A \cup B)$, and by n_σ the number of variables in $(\alpha \cup \beta)$. Then we have

$$(3.1) \qquad N_A + N_B - N_C = N_S$$

Designate by $n_{(\alpha \cap \beta)}$ the number of variables belonging to both α and β. Then, similarly, we have for the sets of variables

$$(3.2) \qquad n_\alpha + n_\beta - n_{(\alpha \cap \beta)} = n_\sigma$$

But by hypothesis we have $N_A = n_\alpha$ and $N_B = n_\beta$, while, by (a), $N_S \leqslant n_\sigma$. Substituting these relations in (3.1) we get

$$(3.3) \qquad n_\alpha + n_\beta - N_C = N_S \leqslant n_\sigma$$

Finally, γ is included in $(\alpha \cap \beta)$ since if a variable is in γ it must appear in C, and hence in both A and B. Therefore, $n_{(\alpha \cap \beta)} \geqslant n_\gamma$. Employing this relationship together with (3.2), we get

$$(3.4) \qquad n_\sigma \leqslant n_\alpha + n_\beta - n_\gamma$$

whence, combining (3.3) and (3.4) and eliminating identical terms from both sides of the resulting inequality, we obtain

$$(3.5) \qquad N_C \geqslant n_\gamma$$

But since, by (a), $n_\gamma \geqslant N_C$, (3.5) implies

$$(3.6) \qquad n_\gamma = N_C$$

which proves the theorem.

DEFINITION 3.3: *We call those self-contained subsets of a linear structure that do not themselves contain self-contained (proper) subsets the* minimal self-contained subsets *of the structure.*

From Theorem 3.1 there follows immediately

THEOREM 3.2: *The minimal self-contained subsets A_i of the equations of a linear structure, and likewise the subsets of variables that appear in these minimal subsets of equations, are disjunct.*

That the subsets of equations are disjunct is obvious from Theorem 3.1. That the subsets of *variables* appearing in the several minimal self-contained subsets of equations are also disjunct follows from the observation that, if this were not so, the sums of minimal subsets with common variables would contain fewer variables than equations, contrary to (a). That is, let A and B be minimal self-contained subsets and let $C = A \cup B$. Then, since A and B are disjunct, $N_C = N_A + N_B$, while $n_\gamma = n_\alpha + n_\beta - n_{(\alpha \cap \beta)}$. But $n_\alpha = N_A$, $n_\beta = N_B$. Hence $n_{(\alpha \cap \beta)} > 0$ implies $n_\gamma < n_C$, which contradicts (a).

3.2. We can now decompose a self-contained linear structure A containing variables α into two parts: a part A', which is the sum of all the minimal self-contained subsets, $A' = A_1 \cup A_2 \cup \cdots A_k$ (containing variables $\alpha' = \alpha_1 \cup \alpha_2 \cup \cdots \cup \alpha_k$); and a remainder, B. Since the A_i are disjunct, $N_{A'} = \Sigma N_{A_i}$. Similarly, $n_{\alpha'} = \Sigma n_{\sigma_i} = \Sigma N_{A_i}$. Hence $N_{A'} = n_{\alpha'}$, i.e., the number of variables appearing in A' is equal to the number of equations in A'. Further, if B is not null ("empty"), we must have $n_\beta > N_B$; otherwise B would be self-contained, contrary to its definition. Hence, at least one of the variables of α' must belong to β.

It is convenient to distinguish three cases:

I. A' consists of a single self-contained set, which coincides with the entire structure; i.e., the structure A contains no self-contained proper subset. In this case B is null, and we may say that the structure is completely *integrated*.

II. A' consists of one or more proper subsets of the structure and B is not null. In this case we may say that the structure is *causally ordered*.

III. A' consists of more than one proper subset of the structure and B is null. In this case we may say that the structure is *unintegrated*.

In all three cases we shall call the minimal self-contained subsets belonging to A' the (minimal) *complete subsets of zero order*.

DEFINITION 3.4: *If in Case II we solve the equations of A' for the unique values of the variables in α', and substitute these values in the equations of B [by (b) this is always possible], the linear structure we obtain is the* derived structure of first order, *a self-contained structure of* N_B *equations in* $n_{(\beta-\beta \cap \alpha')} = N_B$ *unknowns. We can now find the minimal self-contained subsets of the first derived structure,* $B' = B_1 \cup B_2 \cup \cdots \cup B_m$ (complete subsets of first order), *and proceed as before, obtaining Case I, II, or III. If Case II holds, we repeat the process with the* derived structure of second order, *and so forth. Since the number of equations in the original structure was finite, we must finally reach a derived structure that falls under Case I or Case III.*

DEFINITION 3.5: *The minimal self-contained subsets of the derived structure of* k-*th order will be called the* complete subsets of k*th* order.

3.3. By the process just described we have arrived at a complete ordering of disjunct subsets of the equations of A, so that $A = A' \cup B' \cup \cdots \cup N$, the derived structure of highest order, is either unintegrated or completely integrated. Each of the minimal complete subsets, of whatever order, reached in the process may be interpreted in either of two ways. The subset, taken by itself, may be regarded (as above) as a self-contained structure with as many variables as equations, the remaining variables having been eliminated by substitution after solution of the equations of the lower-order structures. Alternatively, it may be viewed as a *complete* subset, in which case the variables in question are not eliminated by substitution but are regarded as *exogenous variables,* the remaining variables (equal in number to the equations of the subset) being regarded as *endogenous variables.* (It will be clear that these terms are used in a sense relative to the complete subset of equations in question.[4])

Adopting the latter interpretation of subsets in the derived structures, it is clear that each complete subset of first order must contain at least one variable in α', for if it did not, the subset would be a complete subset of zero order Similarly, each complete subset

---

[4] This usage of "complete," "exogenous," and "endogenous" is consistent with Marschak's definition of those terms [Marschak, 1950, pp. 7-8].

of *k*th order must contain at least one variable that appears in a complete subset of $(k - 1)$th order and that does not appear in any complete subset of order less than $(k - 1)$.

Since the concepts of endogenous and exogenous variables will play an important role in the following discussion, it will be useful to have for these terms a definition more formal than that just given.

DEFINITION 3.6: *If D is a complete subset of order k, and if a variable x_i appears in D but in no complete subset of order lower than k, then x_i is* endogenous *in the subset D. If x_i appears in D but also in some complete subset of order lower than k, then x, is* exogenous *in the subset D.*

From our previous discussion (in particular, the paragraph following Theorem 3.2) it can be seen that each variable in a self-contained linear structure appears as an endogenous variable in one and only one complete subset of the structure, that it appears in no complete subset of order lower than the one in which it is endogenous, and that it appears in complete subsets of higher order (if at all) as an exogenous variable. Therefore, there exists a one-to-one correspondence between the complete subsets of equations and the subsets of variables occurring as endogenous variables in these equations.

We can now employ the distinction between exogenous and endogenous variables to define a causal ordering of the sets of variables endogenous to the corresponding complete subsets of equations.

DEFINITION 3.7: *Let β designate the set of variables endogenous to a complete subset B, and let γ designate the set endogenous to a complete subset C. Then the variables of γ are* directly causally dependent *on the variables of β (β → γ) if at least one member of β appears as an exogenous variable in C. We can say also that the subset of equations B has* direct precedence *over the subset C.*

We have now partitioned the equations of a self-contained structure into disjunct subsets (the minimal complete subsets of various orders); we have similarly partitioned into disjunct subsets the variables of the structure (the sets of endogenous variables corresponding to the complete subsets of equations); and we have partially ordered these minimal subsets of equations and corresponding sets of variables by means of the (isomorphic) relations of direct precedence and direct causal dependence, respectively.

4. ANALYSIS OF EXAMPLES

4.1. Our first example is the simple one mentioned in the introduction to this chapter:

poor growing weather → *small wheat crops* → *increase in price of wheat.*

We may translate this into the form of a self-contained linear structure as follows: Let x_1 be an index measuring the favorableness of weather for growing wheat; x_2, the size of the wheat crop; and x_3, the price of wheat. We suppose the weather to depend only on a parameter; the wheat crop, upon the weather (we ignore a possible dependence of supply on price); and the price of wheat, on the wheat crop; and we suppose all relations to be linear. The resulting equations are

$$(4.1) \qquad a_{11}x_1 \qquad\qquad\qquad = a_{10}$$

$$(4.2) \qquad a_{21}x_1 + a_{22}x_2 \qquad\quad = a_{20}$$

$$(4.3) \qquad\qquad\quad a_{32}x_2 + a_{33}x_3 = a_{30}$$

Equation (4.1) contains only one variable and hence is a minimal complete subset of zero order, with x_1 as the endogenous variable. There are no other such subsets. Solving (4.1) for x_1 and substituting this value in (4.2) and (4.3), we get the derived structure of first order,

$(4.2a)$ $\qquad a_{22}x_2 \qquad\qquad = a_{10} - a_{21}(a_{10}/a_{11})$

$(4.3a)$ $\qquad a_{32}x_2 + a_{33}x_3 = a_{30}$

We see that equation $(4.2a)$ is a minimal complete subset of first order, with x_2 as its endogenous variable. Solving $(4.2a)$ for x_2 and eliminating x_2 from the third equation, we are left with a single equation as the minimal complete subset of second order. Applying Definition 3.7, we may write:

$$(4.1) \rightarrow (4.2) \rightarrow (4.3)$$

[read: "(4.1) has direct precedence over (4.2), and (4.2) over (4.3)"], and

$$x_1 \rightarrow x_2 \rightarrow x_3$$

(read: "x_1 is the direct cause of x_2 and x_2 of x_3").

4.2. A less trivial example, which also shows that our definitions correspond with common-sense notions of causality, is the structure whose coefficients are estimated by Girshick and Haavelmo in Chapter V, pages 107-110. In writing their system we omit the random terms and employ a different notation for the coefficients:

(4.4) $\quad a_{11}y_1 + a_{12}y_2 + a_{13}y_3 \qquad\qquad\qquad +a_{18}z_8 + a_{19}z_9 = a_{10}$,

(4.5) $\quad a_{21}y_1 + a_{22}y_2 \qquad +a_{24}y_4 \qquad\qquad +a_{28}z_8 \qquad = a_{20}$,

(4.6) $\qquad\qquad\qquad a_{33}y_3 \qquad\qquad +a_{37}z_7 \quad +a_{39}z_9 = a_{30}$,

(4.7) $\qquad\qquad\qquad a_{44}y_4 + a_{45}y_5 + a_{46}z_6 \qquad +a_{48}z_8 \qquad = a_{40}$,

(4.8) $\qquad a_{52}y_2 \qquad +a_{55}y_5 \qquad\qquad +a_{58}z_8 \qquad = a_{50}$,

(4.9) $\qquad\qquad\qquad\qquad a_{66}z_6 \qquad\qquad\qquad = a_{60}$,

(4.10) $\qquad\qquad\qquad\qquad\qquad a_{77}z_7 \qquad\qquad = a_{70}$,

(4.11) $\qquad\qquad\qquad\qquad\qquad\qquad a_{88}z_8 \qquad = a_{80}$,

(4.12) $\qquad\qquad\qquad\qquad\qquad\qquad\qquad a_{99}z_9 = a_{90}$.

Analysis of this structure, which the reader may wish to carry out as an exercise, shows that there are four single-equation subsets of zero order: equations (4.9), (4.10), (4.11), (4.12), and one subset of first order: equation (4.6). The four remaining equations form a single subset of second order in the endogenous variables y_1, y_2, y_4, and y_5. In terms of equations, the precedence relations are

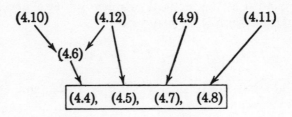

Interpreting this result in terms of the corresponding sets of variables, we find that Girshick and Haavelmo are asserting:

1. That food consumption (y_1), retail food prices (y_2), food production (y_4), and food prices received by farmers (y_5) are interdependent (members of the same minimal complete subset of second order) and directly causally dependent upon disposable income (y_3), last year's food prices received by farmers (z_6), time (z_8), and last year's disposable income (z_9).

2. That disposable income (y_3) is directly causally dependent upon net investment (z_7) and last year's disposable income (z_9).

4.3 We present, without interpretation, a final example:

4.3. We present, without interpretation, a final example:

$$(4.13) \quad \alpha_{11}x_1 + \alpha_{12}x_2 + \alpha_{13}x_3 \qquad\qquad + \alpha_{16}x_6 \qquad = \alpha_{10} \,,$$

$$(4.14) \qquad\qquad\qquad\qquad \alpha_{24}x_4 + \alpha_{25}x_5 \qquad = \alpha_{20} \,,$$

$$(4.15) \qquad \alpha_{32}x_2 \qquad\qquad\qquad\qquad\qquad = \alpha_{30} \,,$$

$$(4.16) \qquad\qquad \alpha_{43}x_3 \qquad\qquad\qquad\qquad = \alpha_{40} \,,$$

$$(4.17) \quad \alpha_{51}x_1 + \alpha_{52}x_2 + \alpha_{53}x_3 + \alpha_{54}x_4 \qquad = \alpha_{50} \,,$$

$$(4.18) \qquad\qquad\qquad\qquad\qquad \alpha_{66}x_6 + \alpha_{67}x_7 = \alpha_{60} \,,$$

$$(4.19) \quad \alpha_{71}x_1 \qquad\qquad\qquad\qquad\qquad\qquad = \alpha_{70} \,.$$

It can be shown that there are three complete subsets of zero order: equation (4.15) and variable x_2, equation (4.16) and variable x_3, and equation (4.19) and variable x_1. There are two complete subsets of first order: equation (4.13) and x_6, and equation (4.17) and x_4. Finally, there are two complete subsets of second order: equation (4.14) and x_5, and equation (4.18) and x_7. In this case each complete subset consists of one equation in one endogenous variable, and we can present the precedence and causal partitioning alternatively as follows:

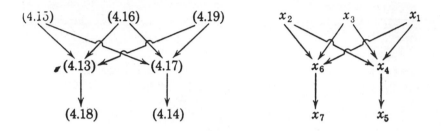

Reordering our equations to correspond with the order of the corresponding variables, the partitioning can also be represented as follows:

		x_1	x_2	x_3	x_4	x_6	x_5	x_7
	(4.19)	×	0	0	0	0	0	0
	(4.15)	0	×	0	0	0	0	0
	(4.16)	0	0	×	0	0	0	0
	(4.17)	×	×	×	×	0	0	0
	(4.13)	×	×	×	0	×	0	0
	(4.14)	0	0	0	×	0	×	0
	(4.18)	0	0	0	0	×	0	×

In this table, nonzero coefficients in the matrix are designated by ×, zero coefficients by 0. The coefficients of the constant term are not displayed.

4.4. We see from this last representation that ordering the

equations and variables according to their precedence and causal relations places the matrix in a canonical form that in a certain sense is as nearly triangular as the structural equations permit. This suggests that calculation of the causal relations in a structure may have some value in indicating the optimum arrangement of equations and variables in fixing the sequence of computation of their solutions. It would be easy to construct an electrical computing device which, even for very large structures, would rapidly locate the complete subsets from this matrix representation:

The blocks of zeros above and to the right of the main diagonal in the canonical form of the matrix show clearly also that our concept of causal ordering is essentially identical with the concept of unilateral coupling, employed in connection with dynamical systems.[5]

4.5 The blocks of zeros in the lower left-hand corner are really accidental properties of the particular partitioning we are studying—that variables of zero order appear only in equations of zero and first order, not in equations of second order.

The causal relation we have defined is a nontransitive relation —$\alpha \to \beta$ and $\beta \to \gamma$ does not imply $\alpha \to \gamma$. We may wish to introduce, among sets of endogenous variables, a transitive relationship meaning "directly or indirectly caused."

Definition 4.1: $\alpha \supset \gamma$ (*read: "α is a cause of γ"*) *if there exist* $\beta_1, \beta_2 \cdots, \beta_k$ *such that* $\alpha \to \beta_1 \to \beta_2 \to \cdots \to \beta_k \to \gamma$. *We may also speak of a relationship of precedence holding between the corresponding subsets of equations; for instance,* $A \supset C$.

5. CAUSALITY IN SYSTEMS NOT SELF-CONTAINED

5.1. We now proceed to show that it is essential that we assume a self-contained structure in order to introduce the notion of causal ordering.

Consider the structure used as an example in Section 4.3. Suppose that we omit equations (4.15) and (4.19) and replace them with

[5] As a matter of fact, the writer originally approached his problem from the standpoint of unilateral coupling (cf. Goodwin [1947, pp. 183-84]).

(5.1)
$$\alpha_{85}x_5 = \alpha_{80}$$
(5.2)
$$\alpha_{99}x_7 = \alpha_{90}$$

We then obtain the following causal structure:

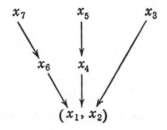

where (x_1, x_2) represents the complete subset of second order comprising the variables x_1 and x_2. We see that we have not only reversed the direction of causation between x_5 and x_7, on the one hand, and x_1 and x_2 on the other, but have also changed the relation of x_3 to the remainder of the structure. Hence we cannot speak of an "internal" causal structure among the variables of a sectional (not self-contained) structure apart from the particular self-contained structure in which it is imbedded. In our new case the canonical form of matrix is

	x_3	x_5	x_7	x_4	x_6	x_1	x_2
(4.16)	×	0	0	0	0	0	0
(5.1)	0	×	0	0	0	0	0
(5.2)	0	0	×	0	0	0	0
(4.14)	0	×	0	×	0	0	0
(4.18)	0	0	×	0	×	0	0
(4.13)	×	0	0	0	×	×	×
(4.17)	×	0	0	×	0	×	×

Of the five equations common to both structures, only equation (4.16) has retained the same order. Moreover, the complete subsets of equations are associated with subsets of variables different from those before.

5.2. In general, we can complete a sectional structure by adding an appropriate number of additional equations, and in general we can do this in a number of different ways. Each of the resulting self-contained structures is likely to have different causal relationships among its variables. One way to complete a sectional structure is to specify which variables are exogenous and to add a sufficient number of equations in which these exogenous variables alone occur [Marschak, 1950, p. 8].

6. OPERATIONAL SIGNIFICANCE OF CAUSAL ORDERING

61. An important objection to our definition of causal ordering remains to be examined—the objection that it is essentially artificial, since the same set of observations could be represented by different structures with different causal orderings of the variables. Consider the following three sets of two equations each:

$$\left.\begin{array}{l}(6.1)\\(6.2)\end{array}\right\} \qquad \begin{cases} a_{11}y_1 + a_{12}y_2 = a_{10}\,, \\ a_{21}y_1 + a_{22}y_2 = a_{20}\,; \end{cases}$$

$$\left.\begin{array}{l}(6.3)\\(6.4)\end{array}\right\} \qquad \begin{cases} b_{11}y_1 \qquad\quad = b_{10}\,, \\ a_{21}y_1 + a_{22}y_2 = a_{20}\,, \end{cases}$$

with $b_{11} = a_{11} - (a_{12}/a_{22})a_{21}\,, \ b_{10} = a_{10} - (a_{12}/a_{22})a_{20}\,;$

$$\left.\begin{array}{l}(6.5)\\(6.6)\end{array}\right\} \qquad \begin{cases} b_{11}y_1 \qquad\quad = b_{10}\,, \\ \qquad\quad a_{22}y_2 = c_{20}\,, \end{cases}$$

with $c_{20} = a_{20} - (a_{21}/b_{11})b_{10}\,.$

All three sets of equations are satisfied by precisely the same set of values of y_1 and y_2 namely,

$$(6.7) \qquad\qquad y_1 = b_{10}/b_{11}, \qquad\quad y_5 = c_{20}/a_{22}$$

Yet the causal ordering in the three sets is different. Equations

(6.1) and (6.2) comprise a single minimal complete set of zero order. Equation (6.3) is a complete set of zero order, while (6.4) is a complete set of first order to which (6.3) is directly precedent. Equations (6.5) and (6.6) each constitute a complete set of zero order. The first structure is completely integrated, the second causally ordered, and the third unintegrated. If the three sets are to be regarded as operationally equivalent, because each can be obtained from either of the others by algebraic manipulation without altering the solution, then causal ordering has no operational meaning.

Closer inspection of the three sets of equations, (6.1)-(6.6), suggests a possible basis for distinguishing them even though they have an identical solution. Consider the first pair of equations. Suppose that equation (6.1) were altered (say, by a change in the constant term or one of the other coefficients). Then the values of both y_1 and y_2 would, in general, be altered. The same would be true if (6.2) were altered.

Consider next the second pair of equations. Suppose that equation (6.3) were altered. Again, both y_1 and y_2 would be changed in value. On the other hand, if (6.4) were altered, only y_2 would be affected and y_1 would remain unchanged.

Finally, consider the third pair of equations. Suppose that equation (6.5) were altered. This would change the value of y_1 but not of y_2. However, if (6.6) were altered, this would change the value of y_2 but not of y_1.

The principle illustrated by the example above can easily be generalized.

THEOREM 6.1: *Let A be a self-contained linear structure, let A_1 be a complete subset of order k in A, and let A' be a self-contained linear structure that is identical with A except for a single equation belonging to A_1. (We assume that the set of variables appearing in A_1 is unaltered.) Consider the (unique) solutions of A and A', respectively. Then (a) the values of all variables in A that are neither endogenous variables of A_1 nor causally dependent, directly or indirectly, on the endogenous variables of A_1 are identical with* *the values of the corresponding variables in A'; and (b) the values of all variables in A that are endogenous in A_1 or are causally dependent on the endogenous variables of A_1 are (in general) different from the values of the corresponding variables in A'.*

Proof: We can solve the equations of a linear structure for the values of the variables appearing in a particular complete subset A_2 by (1) solving successively the complete subsets (starting with those of zero order) that have precedence over A_2, and finally (2) substituting in A_2 the values of all the exogenous variables appearing in A_2 and solving the equations of A_2 for the endogenous variables. Hence, altering an equation belonging to one of these complete subsets will, in general, alter the values of the variables in A_2; but altering an equation in a complete subset that does not have precedence over A_2 cannot alter the values of the variables in A_2.

6.2. Let us apply this notion to the example used in Section 4.1. The structure represented by equations (4.1)-(4.3) might be altered by changing any one of the three equations, each of which constitutes a complete subset.

I. If (4.1) is altered (e.g., rainfall is increased by sowing carbon dioxide crystals in clouds), this will also affect the wheat crop and the price of wheat.

II. If (4.2) is altered (e.g., a drought-resistant variety of wheat is introduced), this will affect the wheat crop and the price of wheat but not the weather.

III. If (4.3) is altered (e.g., a population increase shifts upward the demand schedule for wheat), the price of wheat will change but not the size of the wheat crop or the weather.

The causal relationships have operational meaning, then, to the extent that particular alterations or "interventions" in the structure can be associated with specific complete subsets of equations. We can picture the situation, perhaps somewhat metaphorically, as follows. We suppose a group of persons whom we shall call "experimenters." If we like, we may consider "nature" to be a member of the group. The experimenters, severally or separately, are able to choose the nonzero elements of the coefficient matrix of a linear structure, but they may not replace zero elements by nonzero elements or vice versa (i.e., they are restricted to a specified linear model). We may say that they *control directly* the values of the nonzero coefficients. Once the matrix is specified, the values of the n variables in the n linear equations of the structure are uniquely determined. Hence, the experimenters *control indirectly* the values of these variables. The causal ordering specifies which variables will be affected by intervention at a particular point (a particular complete subset) of the structure.

We see that, in addition to a language describing the linear model, we require, in order to discuss causality, a second language (a "meta-language") describing the relationship between the "experimenters" and the model. The terms "direct control" and "indirect control" are in this metalanguage. Thus, in our metalanguage we have an asymmetrical relationship ($>$)—behavior of experimenters $>$ equation coefficients $>$ values of variables—that must be introduced in order to establish the asymmetrical causal relationship ($\rightarrow$).

In one sense we have moved our problem from the language of the original model to the metalanguage. In order to establish a causal ordering we must have a priori knowledge of the limits imposed on the "experimenters"—in this case knowledge that certain coefficients of the matrix are zeros. If the causal ordering is to have operational meaning it is necessary that, within these limits, the "experimenters" be able to alter at least some equation in each complete subset in some way.

7. CAUSAL ORDERING AND IDENTIFIABILITY

No hint has been given thus far as to the relationship between identifiability and causal ordering. In fact, however, there appears to be a very close relationship between the two concepts, and it is the task of the present section to describe it.[6]

7.1. In Section 6 we sought an operational basis for the concept of causal ordering, a basis that would make of the ordering something more than an arbitrary property of a particular (and arbitrary) way of writing the equations governing certain empirical variables. We found that we could provide the ordering with an operational basis if we could associate with each equation of a structure a specific power of intervention, or "direct control." That is, any such intervention would alter the structure but leave the model (and hence the causal ordering) invariant. Hence, causal ordering is a property of models that is invariant with respect to interventions within the model, and structural equations are equations that correspond to specified possibilities of intervention.

The usual notion of operationalism requires us to associate with each *variable* of an empirical system a method (set of operations) for measuring it. The extended notion introduced in Section 6 requires us to associate with each *equation* a procedure (set of operations) for altering its constant term or coefficients. It is by virtue of such procedures that we can distinguish between "structural" and "nonstructural" sets of equations describing the same set of observations.

But it is precisely this same notion of intervention, and this same distinction between structural and nonstructural equations, that lies at the root of the identifiability concept.[7] As long as structure remains unaltered, identifiability is not required in order to estimate the parameters that are needed for prediction. When a recognizable change in structure occurs, however, identifiability

---

[6] In addition to the logical connection, to be discussed in the text, between causal ordering and identifiability, it may be of interest to point to a number of historical connections. Pioneering work on identifiability was done by Ragnar Frisch [1934], who explored the problem discussed in Section 8.1 below. Other authors in econometrics began to use the concept of causality in their writings without explicit definition; for example, Haavelmo [1944, especially p. 22] and Wold [1949]. An explicit causal ordering for a special class of cases was introduced by Tinbergen [1940].

[7] See Marschak [1950, pp. 8-19], Hurwicz [1950b, pp. 266-73], Chapter I and Section 8 of Chapter II Ando, Fisher, and Simon [1963].

of at least some of the parameters of the structural equations is necessary if correct predictions are to be made in the new structure. From these epistemological considerations we conclude that the conditions under which the causal ordering of a structure is operationally meaningful are generally the same as the conditions under which structural equations can be distinguished from nonstructural equations, and the same as the conditions under which the question of identifiability of the equations is meaningful.

7.2. Parallel with the epistemological relationship just described, we should expect to find a mathematical relationship between the two concepts. In this we are not disappointed.

Identifiability of a linear structure is obtained when certain a priori constraints are placed on the model. For complete identifiability of a structure these restraints must preclude the existence in the model of a different equivalent structure, that is (in linear models), a different set of equations whose members are linear combinations of the original equations.[8]

The simplest basis for identifiability is obtained if we can specify a priori that certain coefficients appearing in the model must be zero. But if the jth coefficient in the ith equation is zero, then the jth variable does not appear in the ith equation. Hence, these specifications may be regarded as determining which variables appear in which equations. In a self-contained structure specification of which variables appear with nonzero coefficients in which equations determines the causal ordering. (In the present section we shall restrict ourselves to a priori specifications of the kind just described.)

7.3. The argument just set forth may be restated in a more

---

[8] The definition of identifiability from which this statement is derived (see Chapter II, Section 3, and Koopmans, Rubin, and Leipnik [1950, Definition 2.1.5.3]) refers to stochastic models. We shall see in Section 8 that the statement remains valid for an equivalent identifiability concept formulated for nonstochastic models [Marschak, 1950, Section 1.3]. In either case, the concept of identifiability always refers to a complete structure, whose equations may be a complete subset (Definition 3.5) of a (stated or unstated) structure consisting of a larger number of equations. The implications of this fact have not received sufficient emphasis in the literature on identifiability, and will be elaborated in Section 8.

formal way, which will perhaps clarify further the operational status of the terms "causal ordering" and "identifiability." An important guiding principle in the relationship between mathematical models and empirical data is that a property of a mathematical model cannot be regarded as reflecting a property of the empirical world the model purports to describe unless this property is invariant under permissible (operationally nonsignificant) transformations of the equations specified by the model.

For example, in Newtonian mechanics it is meaningless to ask whether a body is at rest or in uniform motion in a straight line, for by a trivial transformation of the reference system the motion of the body can be transformed from the first state to the second.[9] It is meaningful however, to ask whether the body is accelerated or unaccelerated since this property is invariant under transformation from one physically admissible reference system to another.

In the classical theory of systems of linear equations we are interested in properties of a system that are invariant under certain groups of transformations of the coefficients of its matrix. In particular, we may be interested in the solutions of any given system (the sets of values of the variables satisfying the system). These are invariant under elementary row transformations of the matrix.

DEFINITION 7.1: *Elementary row transformations of a matrix are those which (1) interchange rows of the matrix (i.e., reorder the equations), (2) add to a given row multiples of another row or rows, (3) multiply a row by a nonzero scalar. These all amount to premultiplication of the coefficient matrix by a nonsingular matrix.[10] The group of transformations thus generated we will call the R-transformations.*

---

[9] This is the classical problem of "absolute" versus "relative" motion. The notion of invariance under transformation as a necessary condition for a "real" property of a physical system has provided a leading motivation for the development of relativistic mechanics and other branches of modern physics. For the identification problems that arise in classical mechanics, see Simon [1947].

[10] Albert [1941, pp. 24, 43].

DEFINITION 7.2: *Any two coefficient matrices that are obtainable from one another by R-transformations we will call R-equivalent.*

Concentration of interest on those properties (e.g., solutions) that are invariant under the group of R-transformations has led to the replacement of the notion of causality by the notion of mutual dependence. For, given a (consistent and independent) set of k linear equations in n ($n \geqslant k$) variables, then, in general, each variable belonging to any subset [Bôcher, 1907, p. 46] of k variables can be expressed as a function of the remaining $(n - k)$.

We have seen that the causal ordering in a linear structure is not invariant under the group of R-transformations (cf. Sections 6.1, 6.2). Hence, to give invariant meaning to this causal ordering we must restrict ourselves to a more limited group of transformations than the R-transformations.

DEFINITION 7.3: *We say that two coefficient matrices are structurally equivalent (S-equivalent) if the second can be obtained from the first by premultiplication by a nonsingular diagonal matrix (i.e., by row transformations of the third type only). The group of transformations thus admitted we shall call the group of S-transformations.*

It is clear that if only the S-transformations are admitted (multiplication of each equation by a constant), the positions of the zero and nonzero coefficients cannot be affected. That is, the causal ordering of a linear structure and the identifiability of its several equations are invariant under the group of S-transformations but not under the wider group of R-transformations.

Now the operational significance of distinguishing between these two groups of transformations has already been suggested in Sections 6.2 and 7.1. If with each equation of a structure we associate a specific power of intervention, then, under S-transformations, this one-to-one correspondence between equations and interventions will not be disturbed—each equation will retain its identity. But, under R-transformations of types (1) or (2), the equations will be scrambled and combined. Suppose that the jth and kth equations belong to different complete subsets. If the jth equation is interchanged with the kth, the interventions will have to be correspondingly reordered; while if the jth equation is replaced by a sum of multiples of the jth and kth, the kth power of intervention will now not be associated with a single equation but with both the jth and the kth.

The definition of identifiability implies that a linear structure is completely identifiable if and only if the priori restrictions on the model (e.g., the zeros of the coefficent matrix) are such as to permit only S-transformations upon the matrix. If the identifiable structure is self-contained, there will then be a unique causal ordering associated with it, and this ordering will be invariant under any transformations permitted by the a prior restrictions.[11]

8. IDENTIFIABILITY IN COMPLETE SUBSETS

The relationship, just explored, between causal ordering and identifiability casts some light upon the conditions under which the coefficients of a structure can be determined from data in the case of nonstochastic models. First, some preliminary explanations are necessary.

8.1 We suppose that we have a large number of observations of the simultaneous values of n variables entering in a linear model. Each observation may be regarded as a point in an n-dimensional space whose coordinates are the values of the n variables. We suppose, further, that the model specifies k equations ($k < n$) which are assumed to govern the behavior of the variables; any single observation must satisfy the k equations. Under what conditions will the observations be sufficient to determine the unknown coefficients of all k equations, that is, the unknown structure within the model?

[11] On the other hand, the causal ordering may be defined even if the structure is not completely identifiable. Since the causal ordering depends only on which subsets of variables appear in which complete subsets of equations, it will also be invariant over the group of R-transformations upon the equations of any complete subset.

The answer to this question can be obtained from geometrical considerations. If each observation is to satisfy all the equations, all observations must lie in a hyperplane of not more than $(n - k)$ dimensions. This hyperplane must be the intersection of the k $(n - 1)$-dimensional hyperplanes representing the k equations. (For example, if there are three variables and two equations, each equation will be represented by a plane, and all observations will lie on the straight line that is the intersection of the two planes.)

Now if the observations do not lie in a hyperplane of *fewer* than $(n - k)$ dimensions, the criteria for identifiability of equations that have been derived for linear stichastic models [12] are also sufficient to assure unique determination of the coefficients of these equations in the present nonstochastic case. For a model satisfying these criteria restricts transformations of the equations to the group of S-transformations (which do not affect the location of the planes represented by the equations), and hence only one set of k admissible hyperplanes can intersect in the $(n - k)$-dimensional hyperplane defined by the observations. That is to say, any other set of k $(n - 1)$-dimensional hyperplanes intersecting in the same $(n - k)$-dimensional hyperplane must consist of linear combinations of the original set, and this possibility is ruled out by the a priori restrictions, specified by the model, that produce identifiability.

However, if the observations are "degenerate" [i.e., lie in a hyperplane of fewer than $(n - 1)$ dimensions], it may be impossible to determine all the coefficients of the structure. Hence, to insure the possibility of determining these coefficients we must require that the variables not be subject to any equations in addition to those of the structure.[13]

8.2. We shall now see how a knowledge of the causal ordering

[12] Chapter II, Section 4; Chapter VI, Section 4.4 and Appendix A, Ando, Fisher, and Simon [1963].

[13] This requirement is a sufficient, but not a necessary, condition for determinacy. If the a priori restrictions are more than the minimum required for identifiability, determinacy may be present even if the variables are subject to additional, unknown restrictions. The problem under discussion here is the question of "confluence," first studied intensively by Frisch [1934].

of a set of variables can be used to help determine whether the coefficients of a linear structure governing these variables can be determined. In the discussion of criteria for identifiability of a structural equation by a linear model, given in Chapter II and in Section 4.4 of Chapter VI, a necessary order condition and a necessary and sufficient rank condition for identifiability are derived. For simplicity, in the following discussion we shall consider only the order condition. The exposition would be considerably complicated, and the results not materially altered, if the rank condition were included as well. In the following theorem we restate the order condition, which, in view of the discussion of Section 8.1, applies also to the present nonstochastic case.

THEOREM 8.1: *In a linear model with a priori restrictions in the form of exclusions of variables from equations, a necessary condition for the identifiability of the k-th equation of a structure A consisting of m equations in n variables is that at least $(m - 1)$ of the variables in A be excluded from the k-th equation.*

It follows immediately that, if A is a self-contained structure, the only equations belonging to it that are identifiable are those containing a single variable (i.e., the equations that constitute complete subsets of zero order). Hence, the prospects of determining the coefficients of a self-contained structure (unless it is made up entirely of one-variable equations) are nil as long as all observations are restricted by the entire system of equations. In fact, in a nonstochastic structure, repeated observations could in this case only produce the same set of values for all variables that was obtained in the first observation. This suggests that we shall need to intervene (see Section 6.2) to "relax" certain of the relationships in order to obtain observations adequate for determining the coefficients of the remaining equations.

In a self-contained structure A consider an identifiable complete subset of S of k equations in n variables. [By Theorem 8.1, no equation of S contains more than $(n - k + 1)$ variables.] If we can produce a set of observations of the variables that satisfies these k equations, and no others independent of these, then we can determine the coefficients of S. Now let us add to S any number of additional equations of A which either (1) belong to complete subsets of the same or higher order than S, or (2) do not contain any of the variables of S. Designate by S' this structure (which includes S).Then the equations of S also satisfy the order condition of identifiability in this new system. For the number of variables in S' must exceed the number of variables in S by at least the number of equations added [by (a)]. None of these new variables appear in the equations of S. Therefore, the equations of S still satisfy the condition of Theorem 8.1 and hence, as far as the order condition is concerned, are still identifiable in S'. We have proved

THEOREM 8.2: *If each equation of a complete subset* S *of a linear structure* A *is identifiable in that subset, it also satisfies the order condition of identifiability in the larger set* S' *that is formed by adding to* S *any equations of* A *which either* (1) *belong to complete subsets of the same or higher order than* S *or* (2) *do not contain any of the variables of* S.

By virtue of this theorem we see that in order to permit the determination of the coefficients of an identifiable complete subset of equations we need to relax, at most, the equations that are precedent to this subset. This theorem makes clear the point, referred to in footnote 8, that identifiability has reference to complete subsets of equations.[14] As a matter of fact, the condition of Theorem 8.2, while sufficient for the preservation of the order condition, is not necessary. Without pursuing the matter in detail, we may illustrate the situation with an example. Consider a complete subset S of k equations in k endogenous and m exogenous variables.

[14] In the stochastic case discussed in Chapter II, Section 3, and in Koopmans, Rubin, and Leipnik [1950, Definition 2.1.3.2] this is reflected in the stipulation that structures are regarded as equivalent only if they give rise to identical distributions of the observations for all values of the "exogenous" variables, i.e., exogenous with reference to the subset considered (Definition 3.6 above).

Suppose the m exogenous variables to be endogenous to a complete subset T (of lower order of precedence) of m equations in $m + p$ $(p \geqslant m)$ variables. Then it is easy to see that, if an equation of S is identifiable in S, it is identifiable in the system consisting of S and T together. To guarantee that the order condition of identifiability will be satisfied when we add new equations to an identifiable complete subset we need merely make sure that we add as many new variables as equations.

8.3 The rationale of the identifiability concept with reference to a complete subset A_k of a self-contained structure A would appear to be the following. We suppose the equations of A_k of order k to be identifiable in A_k, and we wish to determine their coefficients. All the variables of A of order less than k that appear in A_k are exogenous variables relative to A_k. We now suppose that these variables can be arbitrarily varied (by relaxing the structural equations of order less than k) to produce a set of observations of the highest dimensionality consistent with the relations of A_k. This set of observations, together with the condition that the equations of A_k be identifiable, permits us to determine the coefficients.

It is to be noted that we have here again implicitly introduced the notion of an experimenter who, by his direct control over the parameters of the equations in A of order less than k (or by selection of observations provided by "nature"), can bring about independent variations in the variables that are exogenous to A_k. If this procedure is operationally meaningful, the experimenter, confronted with a self-contained structure A, can partition the structure into its complete subsets and, isolating each of these from the whole, proceed to determine its parameters. This seems to correspond exactly to the procedure of a physiologist who (in the example used in the introduction) prevents an animal's saliva from reaching the palate and in this way explores the thirst mechanism.

In the stochastic case nature may provide some of the necessary variability of exogenous variables that escape experimental control. In fact, the discussion of identifiability of complete structures in the stochastic case is meaningful only if sufficient independent variation of "exogenous" variables is provided by nature.[15]

9. CAUSALITY IN NONLINEAR SYSTEMS

Thus far we have considered only the case of linear, non-stochastic structures. In this chapter the problem of causal ordering in the stochastic case will not be considered, but a few comments may be made on the nonlinear case.

We consider a system of functional relations of the form

$$(9.1) \qquad \varphi_i(x, \cdots, x_n) = 0 \qquad (i = 1, \cdots, n)$$

We assume further that the system has, at most, a denumerably infinite set of solutions. Now we can again decompose the system into complete subsets of equations of various orders, such that each subset contains as many variables not appearing in subsets of lower order as it contains equations. If appropriate conditions are imposed on our system, this decomposition will again be unique.

In our linear structure we assumed that an experimenter could directly control the parameters appearing in the equations. In the present case we assume that an experimenter can relax or modify any equation or set of equations in the system. In this way we have the same general relationship as in the linear case between the problem of defining the causal ordering and the problem of identification.

---

[15] See footnote 13 above and also Chapter II, footnotes 7 and 13, Ando, Fisher, and Simon [1963], from which it will be clear that "exogenous" as used in the sentence to which this footnote is appended corresponds to "predetermined" in the context of Chapters II and VI.

10. CONCLUSION

In this chapter we have defined a concept of causality that corresponds to the intuitive use of that term in scientific discussion. Causality is an asymmetrical relation among certain variables, or subsets of variables in a self-contained structure. There is no necessary connection between the asymmetry of this relation and asymmetry in time, although an analysis of the causal structure of dynamical systems in econometrics and physics will show that lagged relations can generally be interpreted as causal relations.

In models specifying which variables are excluded from which equations, the concept of causality has been shown to be intimately connected with the concept of identifiability, although the conditions under which a self-contained structure possesses a nontrivial causal structure are somewhat weaker than the conditions under which it is completely identifiable.

A study of the operational meaning of the causal ordering (or of the concept of "structural" equations) appears to require a metalanguage that permits discussion of the relation between the structure and an experimenter who has direct control over some of the parameters of the structure. As the brief discussion of the nonlinear case implies, the distinction between parameters and variables can be disregarded if the former are regarded as exogenous variables (determined by a larger system) with respect to the latter. In this case the experimenter must be regarded as being able to relax or alter particular equations in this larger system.

REFERENCES

ALBERT, A. A., *Introduction to Algebraic Theories,* Chicago: University of Chicago Press, 1941, 137 pp.

ANDO, ALBERT, FRANKLIN M. FISHER, AND HERBERT A. SIMON, *Essays on the Structure of Social Science Models,* Cambridge: M. I. T. Press, 1963, 172 pp.

BÔCHER, MAXIME, *Introduction to Higher Algebra,* New York: The Macmillan Co., 1907.

CANNON, WALTER B., *The Wisdom of the Body,* New York: W. W. Norton & Co., 1939 (revised ed.), 333 pp.

FRISCH, RAGNAR (1934), *Statistical Confluence Analysis by Means of Complete Regression Systems,* Oslo: Universitetets Økonomiske Institutt, 1934, 192 p.

GOODWIN, RICHARD M., "Dynamical Coupling with Especial Reference to Markets Having Production Lags," *Econometrica, 15,* July 1947, pp. 181-204.

HAAVELMO, TRYGVE (1944), "The Probability Approach in Econometrics," *Econometrica, 12,* Supplement, July, 1944, 118 pp. (reprinted as Cowles Commission Paper, New Series, No. 4).

HURWICZ, LEONID (1950b), "Prediction and Least Squares," Chapter VI in *Statistical Inference in Dynamic Economic Models,* Cowles Commission Monograph 10, T. C. Koopmans, ed., New York: John Wiley & Sons, 1950, pp. 266-300.

KOOPMANS, T. C., H. RUBIN, and R. B. LEIPNIK, "Measuring the Equation Systems of Dynamic Economics," Chapter II in *Statistical Inference in Dynamic Economic Models,* Cowles Commission Monograph 10, T. C. Koopmans, ed., New York: John Wiley & Sons, 1950, pp. 53-237.

MARSCHAK, J. (1950), "Statistical Inference in Economics: An Introduction," Chapter I in *Statistical Inference in Dynamic Economic Models,* Cowles Commission Monograph 10, T. C. Koopmans, ed., New York: John Wiley & Sons, 1950, pp. 1-50.

ORCUTT, GUY H. (1952), "Toward Partial Redirection of Econometrics," *Review of Economics and Statistics, 34,* August, 1952.

SIMON, HERBERT A. (1947), "The Axioms of Newtonian Mechanics," *Philosophical Magazine, 27,* December, 1947, pp. 888-905.

——— (1952), "On the Definition of the Causal Relation," *Journal of Philosophy, 49,* July 31, 1952.

TINBERGEN, JAN (1940) "Econometric Business Cycle Research," *Review of Economic Studies, 7,* 1939-40, pp. 73-90.

WOLD, HERMAN O. A., "Statistical Estimation of Economic Relationships," *Econometrica, 17,* Supplement, July, 1949, pp. 1-22.

Causality in the Social Sciences*

LEWIS S. FEUER

IN the social sciences, man is studying himself. And his basic attitudes towards himself, his hopes, loves, fears, and hatreds, reflect themselves in what we may call his meta-sociological convictions. These, in turn, express themselves in a choice, broadly speaking, between two modes of social analysis, which I shall call the *interventionist* and the *necessitarian*. The interventionist social scientist believes that men can intervene in social situations to change conditions and determine, in significant measure, the direction of trends. The necessitarian believes, on the contrary, that social science can never be used to deflect the lines of evolution, that men's decisions are perturbations in irresistible movements. From meta-sociological beliefs, there thus arise two corresponding types of laws or models, interventionist and necessitarian, which may be characterized as follows:

A law conforms to a necessitarian model if it is one according to which no decision on the part of a person or group of persons can, given the existing social state of affairs, prevent the predictable successive states from coming into existence.

A law conforms to an interventionist model if it is one according to which the decision of a person or group of persons can intervene to alter the existing state of affairs so that it will be followed by states which would not have occurred and would have been unpredictable apart from those decisions.

It is the argument of this essay that contemporary social science is increasingly giving adherence to an interventionist mode of thought. In economics, political science, anthropology, interventionist models are becoming dominant, and scientists are operating on the basis of a meta-sociological principle of interventionism. Before we undertake to justify this analysis of social science, I should like to point out that the distinction between interventionist and necessitarian laws will be familiar to the student of ordinary economic theory. A competitive market, for instance, is described

* From *The Journal of Philosophy*, LI:23, Nov. 11, 1954.

as one in which there is "a large number of buyers and sellers so that the influence of any one or several in combination is negligible." [1] The forms of the laws of supply and demand for such competitive situations are determinate; market prices are unique resultants without equiprobable alternatives, and individual or group intervention cannot affect their determination. By contrast, the laws of monopoly situations allow for the contribution of interventionist decision. The negotiation of wages, for instance, between a strong trade union and a monopolist employer has no unique possible outcome; there is no single equilibrium position, but rather a neighborhood of equally possible wage-rates. The laws of bilateral monopoly are said to have a "zone of indeterminateness." [2] Under such conditions, the action of a single individual or group can materially affect the determination of price. Where domains of indeterminacy are found, sociological laws have begun to lose their necessitarian character.

1. In political science, the greatest example in the present century of a necessitarian classic is Michels' *Political Parties*. The iron law of oligarchy, according to this work, is "the fundamental sociological law of political parties." [3] Michels argued that no movement can hope to produce profound or permanent changes in the social structure. The inevitable tendency to oligarchy, he said, is inherent in all organization. Trade unions, monastic orders, corporations, and socialist parties are all subject to its workings. With masterly realism, Michels drew an impressive documentation for the law of oligarchy from the organization of revolutionary parties. Other investigators had been led to similar conclusions. Sidney and Beatrice Webb, devoted servants of the Fabian ideal, concluded, after their many years' study of British trade unionism, that there is a universal tendency for the primitive democracy of trade unions to be transformed into personal dictatorships or bureaucracies. [4]

[1] Edward Chamberlain, *The Theory of Monopolistic Competition*, Harvard University Press, 1933, p. 7.

[2] Joseph A. Schumpeter, *Business Cycles*, Vol. I, New York, 1939, p. 80.

[3] Robert Michels, *Political Parties*, translated by E. and C. Paul, London, 1915, pp. 401-402.

[4] Sidney and Beatrice Webb, *Industrial Democracy*, New York, 1902, p. 36.

Michels observed the drama of human revolt against the iron law of oligarchy. He counseled the wisdom of resignation. But political sociologists today are often reluctant to acquiesce to Michels' law. They argue that the tendency to oligarchy is neither universal nor necessary; they hold that oligarchic leadership arises under special social and psychological conditions. If most unions tend to become oligarchical, there is still the example of the Typographical Union with its long history of an organized two-party system. If Soviet forms are examples of bureaucratic control, there are also the collective settlements of Israel which are seeking by institutional safeguards to restrain oligarchic trends.[5] A sociology of democratic leadership tries to supplant Michels' law; it investigates the conditions of political apathy, it inquires into the extent to which a proliferation of rival oligarchies weakens their respective internal powers, it applies the psychoanalytical method to power-seeking and leader-craving personalities, it studies how oligarchical trends can be mitigated and controlled. The entirety of these efforts will not as yet measure up to the conviction and evidence behind Michels' law. But the meta-sociological standpoint which animates political sociologists today is clear. They are seeking interventionist models of sociological law which will provide the guide for effective contra-oligarchical action.

From the logical standpoint, what characterizes necessitarian laws is that their independent variables are (what I shall call) *inaccessible*. Michels' law, for instance, holds that as an organization matures, it becomes oligarchical. Oligarchical structure is thus a function of time, and nothing can be done by human intervention to arrest the passage of time. The time-variable is inaccessible. Again, in the case of the laws of the competitive market, supply and demand as independent variables cannot be affected by any individual or group. They determine price, the dependent variable, but they themselves are inaccessible to human intervention in the given context. Interventionist models of causal

[5] S. M. Lipset, "The Two Party System in the International Typographical Union," *Labor and Nation*, Vol. VI (1950), p. 34. Lewis S. Feuer, "Leadership and Democracy in the Collective Settlements of Israel," in *Studies in Leadership*, ed. by Alvin W. Gouldner, New York, 1950, pp. 363-85.

law, on the other hand, are characterized by the quest for independent variables which will be, in large part, *accessible*. If oligarchical trends can be shown to depend on certain specific psychological traits, then intervention on the level of basic personality structure may avail to counteract them. The independent variable, basic personality structure, is presumably accessible through the controls of infant care and child rearing.

2. The power of the meta-sociological principle of interventionism guides social thought in regions where the criterion of verification grows tenuous. A sociological theory wins the allegiance of social scientists not so much because it has more empirical evidence on its side but because it opens up possibilities of human action, of human intervention. The system of economic thought which has become regnant in the last generation is the Keynesian. It is amazing how little verification has had to do with its reception.[6] Keynesian ideas have been accepted not because they explained more than others but because they provided a set of causal laws whose independent variables were accessible to action in the immediate present. Roy Harrod in his monumental biography of Keynes states the matter incisively:

Keynes certainly claimed to be promoting a revolution of thought. The more comprehending critics have had some doubt, on the ground that his main work did no more than substitute one system of concepts for another. In the physical sciences some crucial test is usually available to decide between conflicting theories. If Keynes was really to be successful, he should have been able, it is argued, to refute, say Mr. D. H. Robertson, by showing a set of facts which the Keynesian doctrine would fit, while the other would not. Unhappily the state of economics is not so advanced. It is true to say that the Keynesian scheme consisted in essence of new definitions and a re-classification. . . . In a certain sense one cannot dogmatically affirm one way to be right and the other to be wrong. . . . It is by actual use and application, not by logic, that Keynes has been, and will, I am confident, continue to be triumphantly vindicated.[7]

[6] Cf. Lawrence R. Klein, *The Keynesian Revolution,* New York, 1947, p. 107. Also, Lord Beveridge, *Power and Influence,* London, 1953, p. 253.

[7] R. F. Harrod, *The Life of John Maynard Keynes,* New York, 1951, pp. 462-63.

Underlying the reception of Keynesian theory was the will to intervene in economic processes. When many men are unemployed, and when the social feelings of the economist are genuine, there is a desire to be able to do something about human misery. We don't care to say: "In the long run, the automatic, self-regulating operations of supply and demand will eliminate submarginal firms, and lower wages till the demand for labor rises." "In the long run," as Keynes said, "we are all dead." Not that we can really refute the noninterventionist. Herbert Hoover was convinced that if only we had followed his policy of doing nothing for another six months in 1932, then recovery would have set in. And he ascribes the unemployment of the next decade to the pursuit of Keynesian policies.[8] There is no crucial refutation of this thesis, but it runs counter to the will to intervene which is the response of unresigned men to social crisis.

A meta-economic standpoint, a philosophy of history, was the source of the Keynesian interventionist system of causal laws. Schumpeter has observed that every comprehensive economic theory consists of two complementary but distinct elements. There is first the thinker's vision, his view as to the basic features of society, "about what is and what is not important in order to understand its life at a given time." Secondly, there is the theorist's technique, the apparatus "by which he conceptualizes his vision." [9] Keynes had stated his vision in his early *Economic Consequences of the Peace*. His later theory was the product "of a long struggle to make that vision of our age analytically operative." What was Keynes' vision? In essence, it was a commitment to the postulate of interventionism during an era when impersonal forces might make for the collapse of capitalism. Keynes' mind was filled with images of the struggle between human ideas and an Immanent Will. In one mood, he was depressed by the necessitarian forces of his-

[8] *The Memoirs of Herbert Hoover, The Great Depression 1929-1941*, New York, 1952, pp. 267, 351, 475, 482.

[9] Joseph A. Schumpeter, *Ten Great Economists*, New York, 1951, p. 268. "He was childless and his philosophy of life was essentially a short-run philosophy. So he turned resolutely to the only 'parameter of action' that seemed left to him, both as an Englishman and as the kind of Englishman he was—monetary management." Ibid., p. 275.

tory, and he wondered if a self-destructive impulse inevitably overcame ruling classes. "Perhaps it is historically true," he wrote, "that no order of society ever perishes save by its own hand. In the complexer world of Western Europe the Immanent Will may achieve its ends more subtly and bring in the revolution no less inevitably through a Klotz or a George than by the intellectualisms . . . of the bloodthirsty philosophers of Russia." [10] He spoke of the spectacle of the extraordinary weakness of the great capitalist class, the terror and personal timidity of its individuals. At the last, however, Keynes held fast to the faith that human ideas and individual decision can affect the course of history. The hidden currents beneath the surface of political history, he said, are unpredictable in their outcome. "In one way only can we influence those hidden currents,—by setting in motion those forces of instruction and imagination which change *opinion*. The assertion of truth, the unveiling of illusion, the dissipation of hate, the enlargement and instruction of men's hearts and minds, must be the means." [11] The practical fruit of Keynes' interventionist faith were the proposals in his *General Theory* to apply economic wisdom in fiscal policy and public investment in order to achieve a high level of employment, and preserve the capitalist system.

Whenever the attempt is actually made to verify the efficacy of human decision and attitude in historical crisis, the blind alley of unverifiability besets us. Schumpeter, for instance, affirmed that the decline of the capitalist system does not arise from the workings of an economic pattern like vanishing investment opportunity. He held that capitalism is decaying because of the spread of an anti-capitalist mentality, because profit-seeking is under the taboo of moral disapproval. [12] How can this theory be weighed as against the Marxism or Keynesian? Prolonged economic depression will invariably be accompanied by a loss of confidence in

[10] John Maynard Keynes, *The Economic Consequences of the Peace*, New York, 1920, pp. 237-38.

[11] Ibid., pp. 296-97.

[12] Joseph A. Schumpeter, "Capitalism in the Postwar World," in *Postwar Economic Problems*, ed. by Seymour E. Harris, New York, 1943, pp. 119-21.

the dominant system. To test Schumpeter's theory, we should have to exhibit a battered economy which still preserved the undaunted confidence of its citizens. But we are dealing with inseparable variables, loss of faith and economic depression, which cannot be exhibited in isolation. How shall we verify Schumpeter's theory concerning the causal role of human attitudes? In the end, it embodies like the Keynesian philosophy a conviction in the power of human attitudes to mould the workings of impersonal economic forces.

3. It might perhaps be gathered that the necessitarian mode of thought in economics is the monopoly of the Marxians. Certainly, the Marxian law of the decline of capitalism is a supreme example of the necessitarian model, and its apocalyptic finalism has given to the communist movement a kind of religious exaltation.[13] At the same time, however, it is striking that there is a widespread school which conceives of the inevitable cataclysm of socialism in the same necessitarian manner. The hasty prophets of the debacle of socialism, Hayek and Mises, have evolved a species of dialectical law akin to the Marxian. These thinkers, in Hayek's words, hold that in economic analysis there are "inherent necessities determined by the permanent nature of the constituting elements." [14] In conformity with this belief, Mises, as far back as 1920, argued that rational calculation is impossible in a socialist economy, and that the Soviet economy was bound to collapse. Soviet society, he wrote, is "in a state of entire dissolution," and a "closed peasant

[13] It is noteworthy that according to Stalin, bureaucratic interventionism has terminated the Marxian law of dialectical necessity. The "law of transformation of quantity into quality," he wrote, "is not at all compulsory for a society which has no hostile classes." The transition to collective farms was peaceable and gradual, he declared. "And we succeeded in doing this because it was a revolution from above, because the revolution was accomplished on the initiative of the existing power . . ." (Joseph Stalin, *Marxism and Linguistics*, New York, 1951, pp. 27-28). The political use of doctrines is capable of strange permutations. A movement of social liberation may espouse a necessitarian philosophy, while interventionism, in its bureaucratic version, becomes the apologetic for tyranny.

[14] *Collectivist Economic Planning*, ed. by F. A. von Hayek, London, 1935, p. 12.

household economy" is replacing the disintegrating order.[15] The necessitarian thus held to a simple law: every socialist economy must inevitably founder because it cannot solve the problem of economic calculation.

As the years went on, Mises' prediction remained unfulfilled. But no necessitarian need ever abandon his hypothesis if facts delay its verification. To save his "law" after fifteen years' delay in its working, Mises proposed an unusual modification in its terms. Soviet society, he said, had endured because it was surrounded by capitalist economies from which it derived its standards of rationality. Leon Trotsky held that socialism was impossible in one country; Mises, we might say, held that it's possible only in one country.[16] Still another decade and generation passed by, and the collapse of Soviet economy was still postponed. The economic necessitarians, such as Hayek, have now tended to become sociological necessitarians. They no longer emphasize the prediction of the decline of socialist economy. What they now insist upon is the sociological causal law: that every socialist society must inevitably become totalitarian, because the power of the socialist planners must grow to a dictatorial magnitude. Hayek, therefore, predicted that individual freedom, civil rights, intellectual liberties, would all vanish in a socialist world. It is curious that such critics of socialism have been led to adopt an extreme economic determinism, the principle that the form of economy determines the political superstructure. And the defense of socialist thinkers, notably R. H. Tawney, has been that socialist culture is not bound by a necessitarian law, that human initiative and intervention can help fashion the moral and political relations which will rest on the socialist economic foundation. Socialists today are beginning to

[15] Ibid., p. 124.

[16] "The attempt of the Russian Bolsheviks to transfer Socialism from a party programme into real life has not encountered the problem of economic calculation under Socialism, for the Soviet Republics exist within a world which forms money prices for all means of production. . . . Without the basis for calculation which Capitlaism places at the disposal of Socialism, in the shape of market prices, socialist enterprises would never be carried on, ..." Ludwig von Mises, *Socialism,* translated by J. Kahane, London, 1936, p. 136.

base their proposals not on a necessitarian creed, but on the postulate of interventionism.[17]

4. The quest for a new type of interventionist theory has become most pronounced in the science of anthropology during the years after the Second World War. With the development of programs for technical and educational assistance to the peoples of backward areas, programs associated with the United Nations, the Food and Agricultural Organization, the World Health Organization, and the American Point-Four, the pre-war necessitarian anthropological theory has been receding into a rapid obsolescence. Functionalism was the dominant standpoint in the pre-war years. Some may be surprised to hear it described as an example of the necessitarian mode. But the accuracy of this description can be briefly shown.

Functionalism, in the form which Malinowski gave it, affirms that culture is an "organic unity"; it is the principle that in every culture, each custom, belief, and behavorial form "represents an indispensable part within a working whole.[18] According to this scheme of thought, deliberate intervention to modify or reconstruct a culture is foredoomed to failure. To the functionalist, there are, indeed, no accessible variables in the analysis or control of cultures. To tamper with one institution is at once to rend the fabric of the total society.[19] Each culture is like an idealistic Absolute, a totality which cannot be altered by modifying strategic

[17] A form of necessitarian doctrine meanwhile has been adopted by sociologists like W. Lloyd Warner who argue that "classless societies are impossible" because the division of labor requires supervisory functions. If a group of supervisors is a class, then the existence of classes is a tautological consequence of the division of labor. A necessitarian argument is valid in this sense, but this tautology is scarcely the meaning intended by those who have argued for social and economic equality. Cf. W. Lloyd Warner, Marchia Meeker, Kenneth Eells, *Social Class in America,* Chicago, 1949, pp. 3-32.

[18] Bronislaw Malinowski, "Social Anthropology," *Encyclopaedia Britannica,* Fourteenth Edition, New York, 1929, Vol. 20, p. 864.

[19] As S. H. Roberts stated: "An attack on one part of a closely interrelated native structure usually meant the collapse of the whole" ("Native Policy," *Encyclopaedia of the Social Sciences,* Vol. XI, 1933, p. 274).

segments, an "organic unity" which is disrupted by the crude hands of social planners. The policy consequence of functionalism was straightforward; its practical bearing for applied anthropology was the admonition: don't try to disturb cultures, don't try to change them. Colonial administrators were exhorted not to lay hands upon the delicate patterns of native culture. An imperial preconsul like Lord Lugard was especially praised because his method of so-called "indirect rule" exemplified functionalism in action. The practical value of his standpoint, said Malinowski, was "that it can help the white man to govern, exploit, and 'improve' the native with less pernicious results to the latter." How shall we, for instance, deal with sorcery? Shall we undermine the sorcerer's authority with medical and technological assistance? Malinowski's answer is that "since it invariably ranges itself on the side of the powerful, wealthy, and influential, sorcery remains a support of vested interest; . . . It is always a conservative force, . . . There is hardly anything more pernicious, therefore, in the many European ways of interference with savage peoples, than the bitter animosity with which Missionary, Planter, and Official alike pursue the sorcerer." [20] Those who would manage native labor and exploit effectively the resources of tropical countries would do well, says Malinowski, to study functionalist anthropology.[21] Would it contravene the evidence to assert that functionalism was an expression of the wisdom of a managerial imperialism?

Positivist critics have sometimes suggested that functionalism is nothing more than a tautology. If that were the case, we should be much less concerned with its consequences. It is characteristic, however, of some thinkers that they desire to prove that nobody is saying anything about anything, an aspect of the self-destructive drive which seems to underlie much contemporary philosophizing.

[20] Bronislaw Malinowski, *Crime and Custom in Savage Society,* London, 1926, p. 93.
[21] Ibid., p. 1. "Social Anthropology," loc. cit., p. 864. Malinowski adds: "Since conservatism is the most important trend in a primitive society, sorcery on the whole is a beneficent agency, of enormous value for every culture" (*Crime and Custom in Savage Society,* p. 94).

The functionalist concept in anthropology, however, is used in much the same way as the notion of equilibrium in economics.[22] Where a culture has persisted virtually without change for the lifetime of several generations or more, one can assume that the institutions of its social system have achieved an equilibrium with respect to each other. The religious institutions, for instance, have come to sustain the tribal economy, they raise no voice of criticism, the mythology and folk tales which are prevalent support the political authority, the economy subsidizes the religious leaders. Social institutions are, in the last analysis, founded on human needs, but what is important to observe is that each cultural equilibrium imposes a kind of schedule on needs. It decides which needs are more and less important, it determines the extent to which given needs will be expressed or repressed. Every culture has its unique *repression-expression* schedule, the resultant line of equilibrium located by the interactions of institutions upon men's emotional needs. That every culture is an "organic unity" is a vague way of trying to say something similar to what the economist says when he holds that all the agents of production and consumption in a system are in general equilibrium.

What functionalism, however, has failed to emphasize is that there are cultural equilibria at higher and lower levels of human satisfaction. Keynes dwelled on the fact that there are alternative states of equilibrium possible, each with its respective level of unemployment. An economy can be in equilibrium, despite a high measure of unemployment with the consequent suffering of citizens. Similarly, a culture can be at functional equilibrium with a repression-expression schedule which imposes much hardship upon its members. And such a society, although it's "integrated" and a "living whole," is exceedingly vulnerable to external stimuli; its equilibrium is unstable. The anthropological philosophy as-

---

[22] Cf. A. R. Radcliffe-Brown, "A Note on Functional Anthropology," *Man*, Vol. XLVI, 1946, p. 40. This valuable essay traces the various stages in Malinowski's thought, and records the fact that the name "functionalism" was derived from the functional jurisprudence of Roscoe Pound.

sociated with Point Four recognizes the vulnerability of cultures in unstable equilibrium, and proposes that social science help intervene in the domain of those accessible variables which control the proportions of repression.[23]

Hitherto, the anthropologist in the field has tried hard to be inobtrusive, not to affect the social system which he was observing. The skilled anthropologist has been something like a painter, and it is not surprising that his categories have been aesthetic. When directed change is, however, introduced within segments of a culture, latent dissatisfactions are brought to the surface, unvoiced aspirations for different ways of living are articulated, the degree of intensity of resistances to specific reforms can be ascertained. There are in India, for instance, religious resistances to a program of birth control education. But an experiment in cultural reconstruction has been undertaken by the Government together with the World Health Organization. Does the culture of the Indian peasantry fall apart? Rather the peasants welcome the new program, and urge its extension as a way of dealing, at least in part, with poverty and starvation.[24] The functionalist was concerned to strengthen those agencies which would resist cultural change. The interventionist seeks out the loci of discontent, helps people to express their needs, and renders assistance to those persons and groups who have felt especially the impact of repressive forces, and who would lead their societies in cultural innovation.[25]

[23] As the English psychologist, F. C. Bartlett, has written: "Every culture has its 'hard' or its 'soft' points. If change is first sought at the former, it will provoke resistance and very likely open discord, while the latter are yielding and it is from them that reformation will spread." Cf. "Psychological Methods for the Study of 'Hard' and 'Soft' Features of Culture," *Africa*, Vol. XVI (1946), p. 145.

[24] S. Chandrasekhar, "The Prospect for Planned Parenthood in India," *Pacific Affairs*, Vol. XXVI (1953), pp. 324-325.

[25] See especially the essays of Ralph Linton, Melville J. Herskovits, and Morris E. Opler, in *The Progress of Underdeveloped Areas*, ed. by Bert F. Hoselitz, Chicago, 1952, pp. 109, 126, 90-91. Also, cf. Lewis S. Feuer, "End of Coolie Labor in New Caledonia," *Far Eastern Survey*, Vol. XV (1946), pp. 264-267. Kennard and MacGregor state: "The great opportunity for the anthropologist lies in the problem of the extent to which purposive change can be introduced, how rapidly, and with what consequence to different segments

5. There is a tendency to assume that a necessitarian stand-point, if adopted, applies to all social systems, and the interventionist is likewise apt to extend his model to all history. It may be the case, however, that human decision counts for more in certain social systems than in others. Not even a hero might have prevailed against the forces making for the decline of the Western Roman Empire, and much less than heroic intervention might change hopefully the course of events in our time. A recent necessitarian historian insists that "there was no way out for the Roman Empire." [26] He builds up a kind of immanent dialectical law for its decline: the Empire was based on slavery, the internal market flagged because of the extremes of wealth and poverty, the Roman peace entailed a drying-up of the main source for the supply of slaves. But the necessitarian schemas are never quite convincing. Manumission of slaves became extensive in Rome, and to add to the confusion, if slaves had been needed, their breeding could have been attempted. Moreover, there is always the embarrassing fact of the continued survival of the Eastern Roman Empire for almost a thousand years despite the operation of the same factors that are alleged to have brought Western Rome to its end. Barbarian invasions, the dominance of large estates, the corporative economy, were as much a part of the history of the Byzantine Empire as of the West, but it maintained its existence, nonetheless. [27] The historical pattern is made of unruly material, recalcitrant to designs of inevitability. But at the same time, we find ourselves reluctant to accept the view of J. B. Bury that it was a conflux of coincidences which brought the Roman Empire to its

[26] F. W. Walbank, *The Decline of the Roman Empire in the West*, London, 1946, p. 73.

[27] A. V. Vasiliev, *History of the Byzantine Empire*, Madison, Wisconsin, 1928, Vol. I, pp. 191-197, 417-423. Peter Charanis, "Economic Factors in the Decline of the Byzantine Empire," *The Journal of Economic History*, Vol. XVIII (1953), p. 421.

of the Society" ("Applied Anthropology in Government: United States," in *Anthropology Today*, ed. by A. L. Kroeber, Chicago, 1953, pp. 839-40). Also, cf. Felix S. Cohen, "Anthropology and the Problems of Indian Administration," *The Southwestern Social Science Quarterly*, Vol. XVII (1937), pp. 1-10.

downfall. General causes, Bury held, do not usually explain the great events of history; the chance conjunction of unforeseeable Asian irruptions and a series of incompetent emperors, in his opinion, brought Rome to its decline.[28] Impersonal social forces of a powerful kind do, however, impress one as having been at work in the Western Empire; perhaps the social determinants were not sufficient to constitute a closed necessitarian system, but the margin for human intervention, the degree of freedom which the Roman social system allowed, was small as compared to later societies. Individual decision was overwhelmed in a relatively necessitarian environment. Anything like direct experimental evidence is beyond us with respect to this question, but we can argue that just as economic laws are sometimes necessitarian and sometimes, more or less, interventionist, so the same diversity may likewise characterize the modes of social systems.

The old formulations in the philosophy of social science have become obsolete. The social scientist today is neither historical idealist nor historical materialist; he tends to be what we might call an historical interventionist. He may agree with the Marxian that economic variables are, in many sociological laws, the accessible ones. The importance which sociologists assign to land reform in the Middle and Far East is one such acknowledgment of economic primacy. At the same time, the historical interventionist denies that the fact of human decision can itself be always subsumed in a scheme in which it is dependent on economic independent variables.

Take, for instance, the choice which confronted the Jews of Spain in 1492. On March 30th of that year, the Spanish monarchs decreed that Jews must become Catholics or otherwise leave the country. A few months' grace was allowed for their decision; the Jews furthermore were forbidden to take with them any gold or silver. An inventory of all the facts of the Spanish mode of production, a knowledge of the role of the Jews in the Spanish economy,—none of these economic facts would have enabled us to

[28] Cf. J. B. Bury, *Selected Essays*, ed. by Harold Temperley, Cambridge University Press, p. 66, xxvi-xxvii.

predict the decision of the greater part of the Jews. "Stunned at first by the blow, as soon as they rallied from the shock, they commenced preparations for departure. . . . The sacrifices entailed on the exiles were enormous. . . . There were comparatively few renegades. . . . There was boundless mutual helpfulness; the rich aided the poor and they made ready as best they could to face the perils of the unknown future." [29] Nor was the decision of the Jews the outcome of the influence of some single outstanding individual or individuals. Without a hero to guide them, it was the group which made its decision as to how to act in a great crisis.

6. At every great historical crisis, a situation obtains which we may describe as one of "existential indeterminacy." When the laws of a social system which is breaking down provide no basis for the prediction of the structure of the successor social system, an interval of existential indeterminacy ensues.[30] Let us imagine, for instance, that some primitive society has been making its living through some form of hoe culture. Over a period of years, its population has come to exceed its output of subsistence. A social crisis then confronts the group. What shall be its response? There are, indeed, a number of possible responses to the problem. The society may revise its values to allow for infanticide, or it may decide to destroy its old, or it may embark upon cannibalism. Through chance or inventive genius, it may perhaps discover and adopt a more intensive mode of agriculture; on the other hand, perhaps some warlike leaders will gain the ascendancy, and lead the people into a war for their neighbor's lands.[31] Or perhaps, like the ancient Hellenes, on an arid soil, they will take to the sea,

[29] Cf. Henry Charles Lea, *A History of the Inquisition in Spain,* New York, 1906, Vol. 1, pp. 137-42.

[30] For the significance of indeterminacy in the analysis of economic change, cf. Lewis S. Feuer, "Indeterminacy and Economic Development," *Philosophy of Science,* Vol. 15 (1948), pp. 225-41.

[31] The historian today finds the outburst of aggressive energy among the Mongols in the thirteenth century as much a "psychological riddle" as it was to the medieval chronicler who wrote: "God alone knows who they were and whence they came." Cf. George Vernadsky, *The Mongols and Russia,* New Haven, 1953, p. 5; N. K. Gudzy, *History of Early Russian Literature,* translated by S. W. Jones, New York, 1949, p. 201.

to become fishermen or traders. A society in crisis is in unstable equilibrium; some fortuitous occurrence may then be decisive in determining which of several possible outcomes will be realized. But an exhaustive knowledge of the structure and functioning of the system in crisis will not enable us to foretell by which alternative order it will be followed.[32]

The postulate of interventionism is the assertion that in critical social situations, men can shape their own history; the postulate affirms that human decision can be crucial in determining which of several alternative solutions to a crisis will be realized. To put it in more analytic terms, the postulate of interventionism affirms that, in critical situations, the unknown governing laws are laws in which one or more of the independent variables are accessible. Now there is a temptation to set up an interventionist metaphysics just as there is a necessitarian one. Existentialism seems to me precisely a metaphysics of intervention in the sense that it holds that free choice is inherent in every situation. But the social scientist, we might say, is not a metaphysical existentialist, but rather a logical or methodological one. He finds situations where human freedom is reduced to nullity, where man far from being the captain of his soul is more like a private on fatigue. He finds fortunate conditions under which men are sometimes free. The postulate of interventionism cannot be proved. It is a working conviction of human beings who know at any rate that no necessitarian law of history can be demonstrated. Perhaps, unbeknown to us, the ultimate meta-historical truth may be that man has been lured by a malevolent God to seek for invention, that the inevitable culmination of human history is the self-extinction of the human race through cobalt bombs. The rise and decline of the human race would then be the underlying necessitarian law of history. And the Luddites, the occasional machine-wreckers, would have been the illiterate, unsung tragic heroes who tried to save mankind from itself. Bertrand Russell, indeed, has frequently won-

---

[32] Why, for example, did the Romans fail to develop the intensive agriculture, with the use of excrement as manure, which became prevalent in China and Japan? The historian answers: "We do not know." Cf. Vladimir G. Simkhovitch, *Toward the Understanding of Jesus,* New York, 1927, p. 111.

dered if this were not the truth of things; he felt, as his hope in Soviet communism dwindled, that "all politics are inspired by a grinning devil," and, as he watched Europe on its way to a Second World War, he speculated that perhaps the death-wish was the best explanation of human history.[33] But if such be the underlying law of the macro-social cosmos, we shall never know it.

A directional law of evolution is not logically impossible. The law of enropy in physical science asserts that for closed systems there is a definite direction that energy transformations will take. A directional law of social change cannot therefore be excluded on purely logical grounds. The law of entropy, however, holds only for closed systems; if there were an influx of energy from other parts of an unlimited universe, a given region might not actually evolve toward thermodynamical equilibrium. And laws of history are beyond our grasp precisely because human initiative, human intervention, upsets any approximation toward a closed social universe. The factor of human creativity corresponds to the influx of energy into the physical system. It makes, moreover, for the unpredictable aspect of historical causation. The discovery of atomic fission, for instance, was not something foreseeable from our laws of social science; it was an unpredictable event, dependent on what happened to be the case with sub-atomic events and on the abilities and interests of a small number of persons.

We are once more confronted by the indeterminate aspect of history, the contribution of human individuals, in all its elusive, unresolvable vagueness. A necessitarian law of history may exist, but if so, it does not fall within the domain of humanly constructible laws of social science.[34]

And on this slender foundation, the postulate of intervention-

---

[33] Bertrand Russell, *The Problem of China,* London, 1922, p. 19. "Freud's 'death wish' may be more or less mythological, but on the whole it affords a better explanation of the present behaviour of Europe than is possible on a purely economic view" ("Two Prophets," *The New Statesman and Nation,* Vol. XIII, 1937, p. 416).

[34] "As a transcendental entity there might still be a law of sequence, but there could be no way of demonstrating it." Robert H. Lowie, "Evolution in Cultural Anthropology," *American Anthropologist,* Vol. 48 (1946), p. 229.

ism exists. It is a hope of human beings groping in darkness. The necessitarian may hold that all our interventions have been and will be, in principle, predictable, and he might argue that as human beings we are under an illusion of effective intervention in history, that perhaps an unkind god watches us in our futile efforts to fend off Necessity. It may be that the limits of human intervention will gradually become evident. The countless frustrated efforts to contrive perpetual machines finally provided an empirical basis for the law of entropy. Perhaps a repeated failure of schemes for world peace will similarly persuade social scientists that Freud's theory of the innate aggressive drive in man is sound. But, for the present, there is the rare chance to dare to use the interventionist philosophy. The necessitarian has amended Heraclitus and, instead of saying that "man's character is his fate," declares as a principle of social science that "man's social system is his fate." The interventionist works on the hope that men can, under certain conditions, choose their social world. We act in blindness but in the hope that our action takes us toward light.

NOTES ON CONTRIBUTORS

ROBERT A. DAHL was born in 1915 in Inwood, Iowa. In 1940 he received his Ph.D. from Yale University, where he has taught since 1946, and is now Sterling Professor of Political Science. He has been a Guggenheim Fellow and a Fellow of the Center for Advanced Study in the Behavioral Sciences, and is a Fellow of the American Academy of Arts and Sciences and the American Philosophical Society. He is currently engaged in research on the characteristics and conditions of peaceful opposition in political systems. His publications include *Congress and Foreign Policy; A Preface to Democratic Theory; Who Governs? Democracy and Power in an American City;* and *Modern Political Analysis.*

LEWIS S. FEUER was born in New York City in 1912. He is Professor of Philosophy and Social Science at the University of California in Berkeley and has for the past seven years been chairman of its Social Science Integrated Course. He has written various essays in sociological theory, on Marxism, and American philosophy. He recently published *The Scientific Intellectual,* a work in the sociology of science and philosophic ideas. His previous books were *Spinoza and the Rise of Liberalism* and *Psychoanalysis and Ethics.*

ABRAHAM KAPLAN was born in 1918 in Odessa, Russia. He did graduate work at the University of Chicago and, in 1942, received his Ph.D. from The University of California at Los Angeles. Professor of Philosophy at The University of Michigan, he has also taught at U.C.L.A., Harvard, and Columbia. He has been a Fellow at the Center for Advanced Study in the Behavioral Sciences and the Center for Advanced Studies at Wesleyan University and has held Guggenheim and Rockefeller fellowships. He is the author of *The Conduct of Inquiry; American Ethics and Public Policy; The New World of Philosophy;* and *Power and Society* (with H. D. Lasswell).

DANIEL LERNER, born in New York City in 1917, is Ford Professor of Sociology and International Communication at the Massachusetts Institute of Technology and a Senior Research Associate of its Center for International Studies. During World War II he served as Chief Editor of the intelligence branch of the Psychological Warfare Division, SHAEF, and as Chief of Intelligence in the Information Control Division of the Office of Military

Government, U.S.A. His books include *Sykewar; Propaganda in War and Crisis; The Nazi Elite; The Policy Sciences* (with H. D. Lasswell); *France Defeats EDC* (with Raymond Aron); and *The Passing of Traditional Society*. He also has three previously published volumes in the Hayden Colloquium: *Evidence and Inference; Quantity and Quality;* and *Parts and Wholes*.

ERNST MAYR was born in Germany in 1904, has been, since 1953, Alexander Agassis Professor of Zoology at Harvard University. He began as a student of medicine, Ph.D. 1926, at University of Berlin, and later spent two and one-half years as a naturalist in New Guinea and Solomon Islands. From 1931 to 1953, he was engaged in research on avian systematics and evolution at the American Museum of Natural History (New York). His books include: *Systematics and the Origin of Species; Animal Species and Evolution;* and others.

TALCOTT PARSONS, born in Colorado Springs, Colorado, in 1902, is the major representative of the school of functionalism in American sociological theory and the leading figure in American sociology. He was formerly Chairman of Harvard University's interdisciplinary Department of Social Relations, where he is Professor of Sociology. His books are *The Structure of Social Action; The Social System; Essays in Sociological Theory;* and *Structure and Process in Modern Societies*. He is co-author of *Working Papers on the Theory of Action; Family, Socialization and Internaction Process;* and *Economy and Society* and co-editor of *Theories of Society*. Professor Parsons is a steady contributor to academic journals in all areas of behavioral theory.

PAUL A. SAMUELSON was born in 1915 in Gary, Indiana, and is Professor of Economics at M.I.T. Chicago and Harvard trained, he has been President of the Econometric Society and the American Economics Association, and has written extensively in many branches of economics. He has served as advisor to many government agencies, and was economic advisor to the late President John F. Kennedy and author of the 1961 task force report, *State of the American Economy*. He is presently informal consultant to the U.S. Treasury, the Council of Economic Advisors, the Federal Reserve, and the Bureau of the Budget. He is author of *Foundations of Economic Analysis; Economics: An Introductory Analysis;* and *Linear Programming and Economic Analysis* (with R. Dorfman and R. M. Solow).

HERBERT A. SIMON was born in Milwaukee, Wisconsin, in 1916. He is Professor of Administration and Psychology and Associate Dean, Graduate School of Industrial Administration, Carnegie Institute of Technology. He received his B.A. and Ph.D. degrees from the University of Chicago, and has served on the faculties of the University of California (Berkeley), Illinois Institute of Technology, and Carnegie Institute of Technology. He has published numerous books and articles on organization theory, human decision making, and mathematical social science, among them, *New Science of Management Decision; Organizations* (with J. G. March); *Models of Man; Administrative Behavior;* and *Public Administration* (with Smithburg and Thompson).